Table of Contents

Alcoholism:
Manifestation &
Management

Gary Blanchard, MA, LADC1

© 2021 by Gary Blanchard

ISBN 9798582412809

Also by Gary Blanchard:

Building and Maintaining Recovery

Positive Path Recovery: A Clinician's Guide

Counseling for Medication Assisted Recovery

www.pprtg.org

Introduction

It is hard to find a book that deals specifically with alcoholism that is not more than forty years old. The treatment of substance use disorders has come to the view that addiction is addiction, regardless of the substance. While this is true, alcohol differs from many other mood-altering substances in that it is more socially acceptable than other drugs of abuse.

I decided to compile this book for a class I teach at Anna Maria College in Massachusetts. The class is title Alcoholism Manifestation and Management, and I wanted a book that looks specifically at alcohol. Some early sections on the history of alcohol and treatment for alcoholism are compiled from other sources; I list the source of the information at the end of each chapter. Chapters on treatment are compiled from my other books on treatment of substance use disorders. I hope this book will help people understand the ways that alcohol use disorders are similar and yet different from other substance use disorders.

Part One

Building a
Foundation

Chapter One:
A Brief History of Alcohol

Fermented grain, fruit juice and honey have been used to make alcohol (ethyl alcohol or ethanol) for thousands of years. The ability to metabolize alcohol likely predates humanity with primates eating fermenting fruit We know that fermented beverages existed in early Egyptian civilization.

The oldest verifiable brewery has been found in a prehistoric burial site in a cave near Haifa in modern-day Israel. Researchers have found residue of 13,000-year-old beer that they think might have been used for ritual feasts to honor the dead. The traces of a wheat-and-barley-based alcohol were found in stone mortars carved into the cave floor.

As early as 7000 BC, chemical analysis of jars from the Neolithic village Jiahu in the Henan province of northern China revealed traces of a mixed fermented beverage. According to a study published in the *Proceedings of the National Academy of Sciences* in December 2004, chemical analysis of the residue confirmed that a fermented drink made of grapes, hawthorn berries, honey, and rice was being produced in 7000–6650 BC. This is approximately the time when barley beer and grape wine were beginning to be made in the Middle East.

In India, an alcoholic beverage called sura, distilled from rice, was in use between 3000 and 2000 B.C.

The Babylonians worshiped a wine goddess as early as 2700 B.C. In Greece, one of the first alcoholic beverages to gain popularity was mead, a fermented drink made from honey and water. Greek literature is full of warnings against excessive drinking.

The medicinal use of alcohol was mentioned in Sumerian and Egyptian texts dating from about 2100 BC. The Hebrew Bible recommends giving alcoholic drinks to those who are dying or depressed, so that they can forget their misery (Proverbs 31:6-7). Wine was consumed in Classical Greece at breakfast or at symposia, and in the 1st century BC it was part of the diet of most Roman citizens. Both the Greeks and the Romans generally drank diluted wine (the strength varying from 1-part wine and 1 part water, to 1 part wine and 4 parts water). In Europe during the Middle Ages, beer, often of very low strength, was an everyday drink for all classes and ages of people. A document from that time mentions nuns having an allowance of six pints of ale each day. Cider and pomace wine were also widely available; grape wine was the prerogative of the higher classes.

In the sixteenth century, alcohol (called "spirits") was used largely for medicinal purposes. At the beginning of the eighteenth century, the British parliament passed a law encouraging the use of grain for distilling spirits. Cheap spirits flooded the market and reached a peak in the mid-eighteenth century. In Britain, gin consumption reached 18 million gallons and alcoholism became widespread.

During the early modern period (1500–1800), Protestant leaders such as Martin Luther, John Calvin, the leaders of the Anglican Church, and even the Puritans did not differ substantially from the teachings of the Catholic Church: alcohol was a gift of God and created to be used in moderation for pleasure, enjoyment and health; drunkenness was viewed as a sin.

From this period through at least the beginning of the 18th century, attitudes toward drinking were characterized by a continued recognition of the positive nature of moderate consumption and an increased concern over the negative effects of drunkenness. The latter, which was generally viewed as arising out of the increased self-indulgence of the time, was seen as a threat to spiritual salvation and societal well being. Intoxication was also inconsistent with the emerging emphasis on rational mastery of self and world and on work and efficiency.

Despite the ideal of moderation, consumption of alcohol was often high. In Coventry, England, the average amount of beer and ale consumed was about 17 pints per person per week, compared to about three pints today; nationwide, consumption was about one pint per day per capita. Swedish beer consumption may have been 40 times higher than in modern Sweden. English sailors received a ration of a gallon of beer per day, while soldiers received two-thirds of a gallon. In Denmark, the usual consumption of beer appears to have been a gallon per day for adult laborers and sailors. It is important to note that modern beer is much

11

stronger than the beers of the past. While current beers are 3-5% alcohol, the beer drunk in the historical past was generally 1% or so. This was known as 'small beer'.

However, the production and distribution of spirits spread slowly. Spirit drinking was still largely for medicinal purposes throughout most of the 16th century. It has been said of distilled alcohol that "the sixteenth century created it; the seventeenth century consolidated it; the eighteenth popularized it."

The first confirmed written record of whisky comes from 1405 in Ireland, the production of whisky from malted barley is first mentioned in Scotland in an entry from 1494, although both countries could have distilled grain alcohol before this date.

Distilled spirit was generally flavored with juniper berries. The resulting beverage was known as jenever, the Dutch word for "juniper." The French changed the name to genievre, which the English changed to "geneva" and then modified to "gin." Originally used for medicinal purposes, the use of gin as a social drink did not grow rapidly at first. However, in 1690, England passed "An Act for the Encouraging of the Distillation of Brandy and Spirits from Corn" and within four years the annual production of distilled spirits, most of which was gin, reached nearly one million gallons. "Corn" in the British English of the time meant "grain" in general, while in American English "corn" refers principally to maize.

The dawn of the 18th century saw the British Parliament pass legislation designed to encourage the use of grain for distilling spirits. In 1685, consumption of gin had been slightly over one-half million gallons but by 1714 it stood at two million gallons. In 1727, official (declared and taxed) production reached five million gallons; six years later the London area alone produced eleven million gallons of gin. The English government actively promoted gin production to utilize surplus grain and to raise revenue. Encouraged by public policy, very cheap spirits flooded the market at a time when there was little stigma attached to drunkenness and when the growing urban poor in London sought relief from the newfound insecurities and harsh realities of urban life. Thus developed the so-called Gin Epidemic.[17]

While the negative effects of that phenomenon may have been exaggerated, Parliament passed legislation in 1736 to discourage consumption by prohibiting the sale of gin in quantities of less than two gallons and raising the tax on it dramatically. However, the peak in consumption was reached seven years later, when the nation of six and one-half million people drank over 18 million gallons of gin. And most was consumed by the small minority of the population then living in London and other cities; people in the countryside largely consumed beer, ale and cider.

After its peak, gin consumption rapidly declined. From eighteen million gallons in 1743, it dropped to just over seven million gallons in 1751 and to less than two million by 1758, and generally declined to the end of the century. A number of factors appear to have converged to discourage consumption of gin. These include the production of higher quality beer of lower price, rising corn prices and taxes which eroded the price advantage of gin, a temporary ban on distilling, an increasing criticism of drunkenness, a newer standard of behavior that criticized coarseness and excess, increased tea and coffee consumption, an increase in piety and increasing industrialization with a consequent emphasis on sobriety and labor efficiency.

While drunkenness was still an accepted part of life in the 18th century, the 19th century would bring a change in attitudes as a result of increasing industrialization and the need for a reliable and punctual work force. Self-discipline was needed in place of self-expression, and task orientation had to replace relaxed conviviality. Drunkenness would come to be defined as a threat to industrial efficiency and growth.

Problems commonly associated with industrialization and rapid urbanization were also attributed to alcohol. Thus, problems such as urban crime, poverty and high infant mortality rates were blamed on alcohol, although "it is likely that gross overcrowding and unemployment had much to do with these problems." Over time, more and more personal, social and religious/moral problems would be blamed on alcohol. And not only would it be enough to prevent drunkenness; any consumption of alcohol would come to be seen as unacceptable.

Groups that began by promoting the moderate use of alcohol instead of its abuse- would ultimately form temperance movements and press for the complete and total prohibition of the production and distribution of beverage alcohol. Unfortunately, this would not eliminate social problems but would compound the situation by creating additional problems wherever it was implemented.

Alcoholic beverages played an important role in the Thirteen Colonies from their early days. For example, the Mayflower shipped more beer than water when it departed for the New World in 1620. While this may seem strange viewed from the modern context, note that drinking wine and beer at that time was safer than drinking water - which was usually taken from sources also used to dispose of sewage and garbage. Experience showed that it was safer to drink alcohol than the typically polluted water in Europe. Alcohol was also an effective analgesic, provided energy necessary for hard work, and generally enhanced the quality of life.

For hundreds of years the English ancestors of the colonists had consumed beer and ale. Both in England and in the New World, people of both sexes and all ages typically drank beer with their meals. Because importing a continuing supply of beer was expensive, the early settlers brewed their own. However, it was difficult to make the beer they were accustomed to because wild yeasts caused problems in fermentation and resulted in a bitter, unappetizing brew. Although wild hops grew in New England, hop seeds were ordered from England in order to cultivate an adequate supply for traditional beer. In the meantime, the colonists improvised a beer made from red and black spruce twigs boiled in water, as well as a ginger beer.

Beer was designated X, XX, or XXX according to its alcohol content. The colonists also learned to make a wide variety of wine from fruits. They additionally made wine from such products as flowers, herbs, and even oak leaves. Early on, French vine-growers were brought to the New World to teach settlers how to cultivate grapes.

Colonists adhered to the traditional belief that distilled spirits were *aqua vitae*, or water of life. However, rum was not commonly available until after 1650, when it was imported from the Caribbean. The cost of rum dropped after the colonists began importing molasses and cane sugar directly and distilled their own rum. By 1657, a rum distillery was operating in Boston. It was extraordinarily successful and within a generation the production of rum became colonial New England's largest and most prosperous industry.

Almost every important town from Massachusetts to the Carolinas had a rum distillery to meet the local demand, which had increased dramatically. Rum was often enjoyed in mixed drinks, including flip. This was a popular winter beverage made of rum and beer sweetened with sugar and warmed by plunging a red-hot fireplace poker into the serving mug. Alcohol was viewed positively while its abuse was condemned. Increase Mather (d. 1723) expressed the common view in a sermon against drunkenness: "Drink is in itself a good creature of God, and to be received with thankfulness, but the abuse of drink is from Satan; the wine is from God, but the drunkard is from the Devil."

In the early 19th century, Americans had inherited a hearty drinking tradition. Many types of alcohol were consumed. One reason for this heavy drinking was attributed to an overabundance of corn on the western frontier, which encouraged the widespread production of cheap whiskey. It was at this time that alcohol became an important part of the American diet. In the 1820s, Americans drank seven gallons of alcohol per person annually

Later in the nineteenth century opposition to alcohol grew in the form of the temperance movement, culminating in Prohibition in the United States from 1920 to 1933.

Prohibition in the United States was a nationwide constitutional ban on the production, importation, transportation, and sale of alcoholic beverages from 1920 to 1933.

Prohibitionists first attempted to end the trade in alcoholic drinks during the 19th century. Led by pietistic Protestants, they aimed to heal what they saw as an ill society beset by alcohol-related problems such as alcoholism, family violence and saloon-based political corruption. Many communities introduced alcohol bans in the late 19th and early 20th centuries, and enforcement of these new prohibition laws became a topic of debate. Prohibition supporters, called "drys", presented it as a battle for public morals and health. The movement was taken up the Woman's Christian Temperance Union. After 1900, it was coordinated by the Anti-Saloon League. Opposition from the beer industry mobilized "wet" supporters from the wealthy Catholic and German Lutheran communities, but the influence of these groups receded from 1917 following the entry of the US into the First World War against Germany.

The alcohol industry was curtailed by a succession of state legislatures, and finally ended nationwide under the Eighteenth Amendment to the United States Constitution in 1920, which passed "with a 68 percent supermajority in the House of Representatives and 76 percent support in the Senate" as well as ratification by 46 out of 48 states.[1] Enabling legislation, known as the Volstead Act, set down the rules for enforcing the federal ban and defined the types of alcoholic beverages that were prohibited. Not all alcohol was banned; for example, religious use of wine was permitted. Private ownership and consumption of alcohol were not made illegal under federal law, but local laws were stricter in many areas, with some states banning possession outright.

Following the ban, criminal gangs gained control of the beer and liquor supply in many cities. By the late 1920s, a new opposition to prohibition emerged nationwide. Critics attacked the policy as causing crime, lowering local revenues, and imposing "rural" Protestant religious values on "urban" America. Prohibition ended with the ratification of the Twenty-first Amendment, which repealed the Eighteenth Amendment on December 5, 1933, though prohibition continued in some states. To date, this is the only time in American history in which a constitutional amendment was passed for the purpose of repealing another.

Some research indicates that alcohol consumption declined substantially due to Prohibition. Rates of liver cirrhosis, alcoholic psychosis, and infant mortality also declined. Prohibition's effect on rates of crime and violence is disputed. Despite this, it lost supporters every year it was in action, and lowered government tax revenues at a critical time before and during the Great Depression.

National Prohibition ended on December 5, 1933, with passage of the 21st Amendment. But while prohibition was repealed at the federal level, state and local restrictions on liquor continue to this day.

Section 2 of the 21st Amendment allowed the states to write their own laws governing alcohol. It states that the "transportation or importation into any State, Territory, or possession of the United States for delivery or use therein of intoxicating liquors, in violation of the laws thereof, is hereby prohibited." Subsequent decisions by the U.S. Supreme Court agreed that each state could regulate the sale of alcohol within its borders.

Today, Prohibition's legacy is a collection of archaic and unusual liquor laws that vary from state to state, county to county, city to city, town to town. Some states kept prohibition alive for some time after 1933, with Mississippi the last to hold onto it until 1966. For decades following repeal some states had so-called "blue laws" on liquor until relatively recently. In 2002, 16 states repealed laws banning alcohol sales on Sundays.

Still, in more than a few jurisdictions, alcohol prohibition still exists. About 16 million Americans live in areas where buying liquor is forbidden. Dozens of "dry" counties in the United States – or "moist," with some of their cities wet – remain today, mainly in the Midwestern and Southern Christian "Bible Belt."

Many states permit counties and cities to decide for themselves, by local vote or ordinance, whether to be "wet" or "dry." In Kentucky, 31 of its 120 counties are dry, where selling or possessing booze is a "class B" misdemeanor. Thirty-seven of Arkansas' 75 counties are dry. In Alabama, 24 of 67 counties are dry, with all but one having at least one "wet" city. In Texas, voters in 450 dry municipalities voted to become "wet" between 2004 and 2012, leaving 126 where you still can't buy alcohol. In Nevada, the small town of Panaca is the state's only dry jurisdiction.

Some states allow beer to be sold but not with more than 3.2 percent alcohol content (such as Utah), or a maximum of 6 percent content (West Virginia), even as high as 17.5 percent (South Carolina). Many states cap the alcohol levels in wines sold (in Vermont, consumers may buy wines with less than 16 percent alcohol at supermarkets). Some states, such as Alaska, do not permit alcohol sales in grocery stores. Twelve states still prohibit the sale of spirits (beer and wine are exempted) on Sundays. Indiana doesn't allow any alcohol to be sold on Sundays. Some don't allow sales of beverages on major holidays. Kansas bans it on Memorial Day, Labor Day, Independence Day, Thanksgiving, Christmas and Easter.

Also, there are 18 states with Alcohol Beverage Control (ABC) laws, regulating the wholesale or retail sales of alcohol, except for beer and wine. Some ABC states sell state-produced spirits to independent stores and some only will sell liquor from state-owned stores with limited hours of operation.

One state with a unique history with Prohibition after national repeal is Oklahoma. The state repealed Prohibition only in 1959, but kept strict limitations. Beer above 3.2 percent alcohol content, or "high point beer," is categorized as liquor and may be sold only at room temperature in state-regulated liquor stores. The same went for wine. In 1984, the state finally granted its counties the option to sell liquor by the drink in bars and nightclubs. Later, the state relaxed some laws. Wineries are allowed to sell wine on site. In 2016, the state permitted small "craft" beer breweries to sell their brews with alcohol content higher than 3.2 percent on site without having to use a wholesaler. While four other states also have the 3.2 percent beer law, Oklahoma accounts for about 50 percent of the nation's sales of 3.2 beer.

The variety of state laws shows not only that the Prohibition era has had a lasting effect on society but that people still disagree about regulating alcoholic beverages. Every state has specific laws at least specifying the age people may buy alcohol, hours and locations where alcohol may be sold, the kind of licenses required to sell alcohol in bars, stores, restaurants and to manufacture and transport beer, wine and hard liquor (distilled spirits such as whiskey, vodka and gin).

While it's legal today to make wine and beer at home for personal or family use, running an old-fashioned "still" to concoct spirits or making gin in a bathtub remain felony crimes under federal law. The U.S. government since the end of Prohibition has legal jurisdiction and oversight over the manufacturing of liquor intended for sale. Owners of breweries, wineries and hard liquor-making distilleries seeking to sell their wares must obtain a federal permit from the U.S. Treasury Department before making anything, and then pay federal taxes on every gallon they produce. States, counties and cities also set their own taxes on liquor sales.

In fact, liquor taxes are an important source of government revenue. The industry is among the highest taxed in the country along with tobacco. The federal tax is $7 to $18 per barrel for beer, $1 to $3.40 per gallon for wine and $13.50 per proof gallon of spirits. The combination of federal, state and local taxes adds a hefty premium to the price of a bottle of alcohol. In Chicago, for instance, the tax rate on a 750-milliliter bottle of distilled liquor (such as vodka), including federal, state, city and county taxes, plus state and local sales taxes, would amount to 28 percent.

In 2014, the U.S. government levied $7.9 billion in federal excise taxes on liquor, which by federal estimates is a $400 billion to $500 billion per year industry employing about four million people. The states received about $6.1 billion in alcohol taxes that year.

Another legacy of Prohibition is that Americans are drinking less. Before Prohibition began in 1920, the average American drank 2.6 gallons of alcohol each year. That average, even with speakeasies and the bootlegged liquor, dropped by more than 70 percent in the early years of Prohibition. After its repeal, Americans did not return to the pre-Prohibition drinking level until 1973. Since the mid-1980s, annual consumption has fallen to about 2.2 gallons per person. The United States does not even make the list of the top ten countries with the highest consumption of liquor. Number one is the small nation of Luxembourg, at 4.11 gallons per capita, then Ireland at 3.62 gallons and Hungary with 3.59 gallons.

(This chapter was compiled from articles in Wikipedia and from the website of The Mob Museum.)

Chapter Two:
A Brief History of Addiction Treatment in the United States

In the early 1750's to Early 1800s Alcoholic mutual aid societies (sobriety "Circles") were formed within various Native American tribes. Some were part of, or evolved into, abstinence-based Native American cultural revitalization movements and temperance organizations. In 1774, Anthony Benezet's *Mighty Destroyer Displayed* was published. It is the earliest American essay on alcoholism.

It was in 1784 that Dr. Benjamin Rush's *Inquiry into the Effects of Ardent Spirits on the Human Mind and Body* catalogued the consequence of chronic drunkenness and argued that this condition is a disease that physicians should be treating. Rush's writing marked the beginning of American temperance movement. It was also the first time the disease concept of addition was presented. In 1810 Dr. Benjamin Rush called for creation of a "Sober House" for the care of the confirmed drunkard. (As you can see, Dr. Rush was ahead of his times.)

In 1825, Rev. Lyman Beecher's *Six Sermons on Intemperance* described those "addicted to the sin" of intemperance, and noted presence of an "insatiable desire to drink," and described warning signs of addiction to distilled spirits. Then in 1830 Dr. Samuel Woodward called for creation of inebriate asylums.

It was in 1840 that The Washingtonian Society, organized by and for "hard cases," would grow to more than 600,000 members before its precipitous decline in the mid-1840s. Many local Washingtonian groups were replaced by a new social institution -- the Fraternal Temperance Society, some of which were organized exclusively for "reforming" men. (You will notice that women are not seen to be susceptible to alcohol problems at the time.)

In 1844 – 1845, Lodging Homes and later (in 1857) a Home for the Fallen are opened in Boston -- marking the roots of the 19th century inebriate home. As inebriate homes spread, they will spawn several alcoholic mutual aid societies such as the Godwin Association. Also in 1845, Frederick Douglass (having earlier acknowledged a period of intemperance in his life) signs a pledge of abstinence and becomes involved in promoting temperance among African American people. His call for abstinence as a foundation of the drive to abolish slavery and prepare Black people for full citizenship anticipated modern Afrocentric models of addiction recovery.

It was in 1849 that the Swedish physician Magnus Huss described a disease resulting from chronic alcohol consumption and christened it Alcoholismus chronicus. This marks the introduction of the term alcoholism. In 1864 the New York State Inebriate Asylum, the first in the country, opened in Binghamton, NY. A growing network of inebriate asylums would treat alcoholism and addiction to a growing list of other drugs: opium, morphine, cocaine, chloral, ether, and chloroform.

The opening of the Martha Washington Home in Chicago in 1867 marked the first institution in America that specialized in the treatment of inebriate women. In 1870 the American Association for the Cure of Inebriety was founded under the principle "Inebriety is a disease." The Association's Journal of Inebriety is published from 1876-1914.

By the 1870s, new alcoholic mutual aid societies - the Ribbon Reform Clubs -- began in the Northeast and spread throughout the U.S. over the next two decades. They were named for their members' practice of wearing a colored ribbon on their clothing so that they could recognize one another and convey a message of hope about recovery to the larger community.

In 1872 Jerry McAuley opened the Water Street Mission in New York City, marking the beginning of the urban mission movement. This movement, spread across America by the Salvation Army, catered its message and services to the "Skid Row." The urban missions would birth such alcoholics mutual aid societies as the United Order of Ex-Boozers. The missions were linked to religiously oriented, rural inebriate colonies.

It was in 1879 that Dr. Leslie Keeley announced that "Drunkenness is a disease and I can cure it." He opened more than 120 Keeley Institutes across the U.S., marking the beginning of franchised, private, for-profit addiction treatment institutes/sanatoria in America.

Then in the 1880s, Cocaine was recommended by Sigmund Freud and a number of American physicians in the treatment of alcoholism and morphine addiction. Bottled home cures for the alcohol and drug habits abounded; most would be later exposed to contain alcohol, opium, morphine, cocaine and cannabis. In 1891 – 1892 the Keeley League (a Keeley Institute patient mutual aid society) was founded. Keeley League members meet under the banner, "The Law Must Recognize a Leading Fact: Medical Not Penal Treatment Reforms the Drunkard."

By the early 1900, as inebriate homes and asylums closed, alcoholics were relegated to city "drunk tanks," "cells" in "foul wards" of public hospitals, and the back wards of aging "insane asylums." Wealthy alcoholics/addicts would continue to seek discrete detoxification in private sanatoria known as "jitter joints," "jag farms" or "dip shops."

In 1901, the Charles B. Towns Hospital for Drug and Alcoholic Addictions in New York City marked the beginning of a new type of private "drying out" hospital for affluent alcoholics and addicts. Then in 1906, the Emmanuel Clinic in Boston began the practice of lay therapy in the treatment of alcoholism. The Clinic would generate a number of noted lay therapists (Baylor, Chambers, Peabody) who came to exert enormous influence on alcoholism treatment for several decades. The Jacoby Club served as the Clinic's mutual aid society.

Between 1907-1913 the first of two waves of state laws were passed that called for the mandatory sterilization of "defectives": the mentally ill, the developmentally disabled, and alcoholics and addicts. Then in 1914 the Harrison Tax Act brought opiates and cocaine under federal control and placed physicians as the gatekeepers for access to these drugs.

A 1919 Supreme Court decision (Webb v. the United States) declared that for a physician to maintain an addict on his or her customary dose is not a "good faith" medical practice under the Harrison Act and thus an indictable offense. Some 25,000 physicians are indicted for violations of this act between 1919 and 1935.

Between the years 1919-1924, forty-four communities established morphine maintenance clinics (run by public health departments or police departments) to care for incurable and medically infirm addicts. All eventually closed under threat of federal indictment. Treatment for narcotic addiction virtually disappeared for all but the most affluent Americans. Then most inebriate homes, inebriate asylums and private addiction cure institutes collapsed between 1910 and 1925. The Journal of Inebriety ceased publication in 1914 and its parent association collapsed in the early 1920s.

In 1935 the opening of Shadel Sanatorium marked the introduction of aversive conditioning in an institutional alcoholism treatment setting. At the same time, the first federal "narcotics farm" (U.S. Public Health Prison Hospital) opened in Lexington, Kentucky. The second facility opened in Fort Worth, Texas in 1938. This marked the beginning of federal involvement in addiction research and addiction treatment.

Another major event that happened in 1935 was the meeting of Bill W. and Dr. Bob S. (and Dr. Bob's last drink), marking the beginning of Alcoholics Anonymous (AA). In 1937 The Research Council on Problems of Alcohol brought prominent scientists into the study of alcohol-related problems. Then in 1939 the book, *Alcoholics Anonymous*, also known as "the big book" was published.

In June, 1940 the first issue of the Quarterly Journal of Studies on Alcohol was published. In 1940 – 1945, recovered alcoholics in AA were recruited at Remington Arms, DuPont, Kaiser Shipyards, and North American Aviation to work in the first modern industrial alcoholism programs -- forerunners of today's employee assistance programs (EAPS). In 1941 a Saturday Evening Post article on AA sparked a period of dramatic growth and geographical dispersion of AA. Then in 1942 Dwight Anderson of the Research Council on Problems of Alcohol called for a sustained campaign of public education to alter American's view of alcoholism and the alcoholic.

In 1943 the Yale Center of Alcohol studies initiated a significant research program, the Summer School of Alcohol Studies, the Yale Plan Outpatient Clinics, and the Yale Plan for Business and Industry. The Center would move to Rutgers in 1962.

In another major event in 1944, Marty Mann founded the National Committee for Education on Alcoholism (today the National Council on Alcoholism and Drug Dependence) around the following propositions:

1. Alcoholism is a disease.

2. The alcoholic, therefore, is a sick person.

3. The alcoholic can be helped.

4. The alcoholic is worth helping.

5. Alcoholism is our No. 4 public health problem, and our public responsibility.

Mann called for a five-prong approach to be achieved by local NCEA affiliates:

1. Launching local public education campaigns on alcoholism.

2. Encouraging hospitals to admit alcoholics for acute detoxification.

3. Establishing local alcohol information centers.

4. Establishing local clinics for the diagnosis and treatment of alcoholism.

5. Establishing "rest centers" for the long-term care of alcoholics.

The first state alcoholism commissions were founded; they supported fledgling efforts at local community education and treatment.

Between 1944 - 1947 a new body of alcoholism-themed literature was published: *The Lost Weekend* (1944), *September Remembers* (1945), *Breakdown* (1946), *Devil by the Tail* (1947), *If a Man be Mad* (1947), and *Under the Volcano* (1947).

In 1947 an Addicts Anonymous group began meeting at the U.S. Public Health Hospital in Lexington, Kentucky. Meetings began outside the institution in New York City under the name Narcotics Anonymous (NA) in 1949 but dissipated over time. The roots of today's NA can be traced to groups that began in California in 1953.

In 1948, Alcoholics Victorious was founded within the Chicago Christian Industrial League and spread as a Christian, recovery support group within many of the nation's urban missions. Between 1948 - 1950 the "Minnesota Model" of chemical dependency treatment emerged in the synergy between three institutions: Pioneer House, Hazelden, and Willmar State Hospital. Disulfram (Antabuse) was introduced as an adjunct in the treatment of alcoholism in the U.S. Other drugs used in the treatment of alcoholism during this period include barbiturates, amphetamines (Benzedrine), and LSD.

The year of 1950 played a major role in the history of addiction treatment in America. It was in 1950 that the Twelve Traditions were formally adopted to govern the group life of AA. The National Institute of Mental Health established a special division on alcoholism. Marty Mann's *Primer on Alcoholism* was published. The American Medical Association (AMA) resolved to create a special committee to develop a program for "medicine's aggressive participation in the work of solving the problems of alcoholism."

In the early 1950s, AA membership surpassed 90,000 as America (and Hollywood) became interested in the subject of alcoholism. Cinema portrayal of alcoholism includes such noted films *as Lost Weekend, Days of Wine and Roses, and Come Back, Little Sheba.* Also in the 1950s the halfway house movement culminated in the founding (1958) of the Association of Halfway House Alcoholism Programs of North America.

In 1951 Lois W. and Anne B. start a Clearing House for the growing number of Family Groups that had grown in tandem with AA through the 1940s. The opening of the Clearing House marked the formal organization of these groups into Al-Anon Family Groups.

It was in 1952 that the American Medical Association first defined alcoholism. R. Brinkley Smithers established the Christopher D. Smithers Foundation, a charitable organization that focused its primary mission on the support of alcoholism education and treatment efforts. This focus followed Smithers' own recovery from alcoholism and his participation in the Yale Summer School of Alcohol Studies. By the mid-1990s, the Foundation and the Smithers family had donated more than $37 million to support alcoholism-related projects.

In 1954 Ruth Fox, MD established the New York City Medical Society on Alcoholism, today known as the American Society of Addiction Medicine (ASAM). The Minnesota State Civil Service Commission became the first such body in the United States to approve a state job classification position for "Counselor on Alcoholism."

In 1956 the American Medical Association stopped short of declaring alcoholism a disease but did recognize alcoholics as legitimate patients: They stated, "Hospitals should be urged to consider admission of such patients with a diagnosis of alcoholism based upon the condition of the individual patient, rather than a general objection to all such patients."

In 1957 the Veteran's Health Administration began developing alcoholism treatment units within its national network of VA hospitals. The American Hospital Association passed a resolution to help prevent discrimination against alcoholics. The Fordham University School of Social Services offered the first full university course on alcoholism for credit. In 1958 the first ex-addict-directed therapeutic community - Synanon -- was founded by Charles Dederich. It would be widely replicated in the 1960s and 1970s.

In 1960, E.M. Jellinek published *The Disease Concept of Alcoholism*. In the early 1960s several states initiated civil commitment programs for narcotic addicts. Then, in 1961 the American Bar Association/American Medical Association (ABA/AMA) report, *Drug Addiction: Crime or Disease?*, called for community-based treatment programs.

It was in 1963 when the American Public Health Association adopted an official statement on alcoholism, identifying it as a treatable illness. Between 1963 and 1966 provision for local alcoholism and addiction counseling were included in federal legislation funding the

34

development of local comprehensive community mental health centers, anti-poverty programs, and criminal justice diversion programs. Such federal funding increased throughout the 1960s. As alcoholism programs spread, there was heated debate over the question of who is qualified to treat the alcoholic. Tensions abound between "paraprofessional" recovering alcoholics and psychiatrists, psychologists and social workers within newly emerging alcoholism treatment programs.

Another major event in treatment history came in 1964 when Dr. Vincent Dole, an endocrinologist, and Dr. Marie Nyswander, a psychiatrist specializing in addiction, introduced methadone blockade therapy in the treatment of narcotic addiction. Between 1964 and 1975 the insurance industry began to reimburse the treatment of alcoholism on par with the treatment of other illnesses. This led to a dramatic expansion in private and hospital-based inpatient treatment programs. In 1965 the American Psychiatric Association urged its members to learn about alcoholism and urged that health insurance plans cover alcoholism treatment.

In 1966 two federal Appeals Court decisions supported the disease concept of alcoholism. President Johnson appointed the first National Advisory Committee on Alcoholism and became the first President to address the country about alcoholism. He proclaimed: "The alcoholic suffers from a disease which will yield eventually to scientific research and adequate treatment." The National Center for the Prevention and Control of

Alcoholism was created within the National Institute on Mental Health. The Narcotic Addict Rehabilitation Act (NARA) marks a milestone of increased federal involvement in supporting development of local addiction treatment services.

In 1967 the Cooperative Commission on the Study of Alcoholism released its report, *Alcohol Problems: A Report to the Nation*. The Report called for a national action plan, including the establishment of a national center on alcoholism to lead a national effort in alcoholism research, education, and treatment. The American Medical Association passed a resolution identifying alcoholism as a "complex" disease and a "disease that merits the serious concern of all members of the health professions." The New York Medical Society altered its mission to become the American Society on Addiction Medicine.

Between 1967 and 1971, special alcoholism counseling and treatment initiatives began within all major branches of the U.S. Armed Forces. In 1968 the Federal Advisory Committee on Traffic Safety acknowledged the substantial role alcohol plays in car crashes. Federal agencies in the early 1970s, through the Alcohol Safety Action Program, promoted new impaired driving laws and the rise of remedial education, assessment/referral/treatment services for those arrested for alcohol-impaired driving.

Then, in 1970, Congress passed the "Comprehensive Alcohol Abuse and Alcoholism Prevention Treatment and Rehabilitation Act," known as the Hughes Act for its sponsor in the

Senate, Harold E. Hughes. The legislation established the National Institute on Alcohol Abuse and Alcoholism (NIAAA). Those testifying in support of the legislation include Marty Mann of NCA and Bill Wilson, Co-founder of AA.

In 1971 The American Journal of Psychiatry and the Annals of Internal Medicine publish the *"Criteria for the Diagnosis of Alcoholism."* The National States Conference of Commissioners on Uniform States Laws adopted the Uniform Alcoholism and Intoxication Act. This led to the progressive decriminalization of public intoxication and the emergence of social setting detoxification centers across the United States. The Association of Labor-Management Administrators and Consultants on Alcoholism, now known as the Employee Assistance Professionals Association, met for the first time. The American College of Internal Medicine included alcoholism questions on the board examinations.

1972 was another major year in the history of addiction treatment. In that year, The Joint Commission on Accreditation of Hospitals developed accreditation standards for alcoholism treatment programs. The Alcoholism Report, the first newsletter devoted exclusively to the field of alcoholism, began publication. The National Association of Alcoholism Counselors and Trainers was founded at a meeting of Organization for Economic Opportunity regional alcoholism programs. It evolved into the National Association of Alcoholism and Drug Abuse Counselors (NAADAC). The Food and Drug Administration approved use of methadone for treating heroin addiction. The Drug Abuse Treatment Act of 1972 created the Special Action Office for Drug Abuse Prevention that laid the groundwork for the creation of the National Institute on Drug Abuse in 1974. TASC (Treatment Alternatives to Street Crime) was created by the Drug Abuse and Treatment Act to screen addicts in the criminal justice system and then to link and manage their involvement in treatment services.

In 1973 U.S. investigators first described fetal alcohol syndrome (FAS), a pattern of birth defects observed in children born to alcoholic mothers. Vernon Johnson's book, *I'll Quit Tomorrow*, introduced intervention technologies that are still widely used to reach alcoholics and addicts before they "hit bottom."

In 1974 the first of a series of studies on credentialing of counselors working in alcohol and drug treatment programs marked the beginning of a sustained process of certification and licensure of addiction counselors. In the Mid 1970s arguments raged over whether alcoholism and "drug abuse" treatment (which have been separate fields for most of the 20th century) should be administratively and clinically merged. Such integration would become widespread at the state and local (but not the national) levels during the 1980s.

It was in 1975 that the Federal White Paper on Drug Abuse recommended expanded federal support for addiction treatment. Women for Sobriety was founded by Dr. Jean Kirkpatrick.

In 1980 President Carter appointed the National Commission on Alcoholism and Other Alcohol Related Problems, chaired by Senator Harold Hughes. It only met once. Mothers Against Drunk Driving, a powerful grassroots advocacy group, was formed in 1980 In 1981 the U.S. Postal Service issued a first-class stamp imprinted with "Alcoholism. You can beat it!" Nancy Reagan's "Just Say No" anti-drug campaign was launched within a broader "zero tolerance" campaign that reduced federal support for treatment and marked the beginning of the dramatic rise in the number of drug users who were incarcerated. The growth of addicted offenders in the 1980s led to the demand for drug courts and in-prison treatment in the 1990s.

In 1982 the federal Block Grant Program transferred responsibility for the delivery of treatment and prevention services to the states. Former First Lady Betty Ford lent her name to a treatment center for alcoholism and other drug addictions. Cocaine Anonymous was founded. Between 1982 - 1992 the number of women-only treatment units tripled as NIAAA and NIDA focused attention on the special needs of addicted women.

In 1983 the first certification exam for addiction medicine specialty was offered in California, and the National Association for Children of Alcoholics was founded. In 1984 the National Minimum Drinking Age Act required all states to make purchase or public possession of alcoholic beverages illegal for anyone under the age of 21 or they would lose federal funding for highways. This reflects a growing concern about the lowered age of alcohol use.

Then, in 1985, Time magazine heralded the "new temperance" movement. The first appearance of crack cocaine focused enormous public attention on the illegal drug problem. Concerns about cocaine-exposed infants led to expansion of treatment resources for women and specialized programs to treat women involved in the child protection system. The American Academy of Psychiatrists in Alcoholism and Addictions was founded. In 1985 - 1986 the founding of Secular Organization for Sobriety and Rational Recovery marked the growing pluralism within the American culture of recovery.

Between 1985 - 1990, addiction treatment became increasingly concerned about "special populations" and launched specialized treatment tracks for women, adolescents, the elderly, gays and lesbians, and the "dually diagnosed." As the challenges of treating new patterns of cocaine addiction grew, relapse tracks also become a common treatment innovation.

The 1986 Anti-Drug Abuse Act authorized $4 billion to fight drugs, primarily through law enforcement. President Reagan issued an executive order mandating the federal Drug-Free Workplace program. This marked a shift in focus from the linkage of drug-impaired workers to treatment/recovery resources to the referral of drug-using employees to such resources.

In 1987 President Reagan formally announced a renewed "War on Drugs"; the shift away from treatment toward punishment and incarceration intensified at that point. The American Medical Association called all drug dependencies diseases whose treatment is a legitimate part of medical practice.

In 1988 the U.S. Supreme Court declined to overturn a Veteran's Administration regulation -- later changed by an act of Congress -- that classified alcoholism as "willful misconduct." The American Society of Addiction Medicine awarded a seat in the American Medical Association's house of delegates.

The publication of Stanton Peele's *Diseasing of America: Addiction Treatment Out of Control* in 1989 marked the full emergence of a movement whose primary mission was opposition to Twelve Step programs and Twelve Step-oriented addiction treatment. The first specialized "drug court" was started by Miami Judge Stanley Goldstein. It spurred a national movement to link addicted, non-violent offenders to treatment as an alternative to incarceration.

From 1989 – 1994, following an erosion of alcoholism treatment reimbursement benefits by insurance carriers, an aggressive system of managed care all but eliminated the 28-day inpatient treatment program in hospitals and private, free-standing centers. The downsizing and closure of hospital-based treatment units sparked a trend toward the integration of many psychiatric and addiction treatment units and a renewed community trend of incorporating addiction treatment services under the umbrella of mental health or "behavioral health" services. Most inpatient treatment programs shifted their emphasis toward outpatient and intensive outpatient services. The loss of residential services added fuel to a growing recovery home movement.

During the 1990s the explosive growth of the internet led to a proliferation of on-line recovery support groups and services, creating a virtual recovering community without geographical boundaries. (This would become a big benefit during the Covid-19 Pandemic in 2020.) In 1990, Senator Harold Hughes founded the Society of Americans for Recovery (SOAR). NCA changes its name to National Council on Alcoholism and Drug Dependence -- marking a significant milestone in the integration of the alcoholism and drug abuse fields.

In 1991, The American Society of Addiction Medicine published its ASAM Patient Placement Criteria for the Treatment of Psychoactive Substance Use Disorders. The ASAM criteria shifted treatment toward a "levels of care" system rather than a single modality indiscriminately applied to all those entering treatment. Between 1992 and 1997, a resurgence in youthful polydrug experimentation spurred interest in the development of effective adolescent treatment approaches. In 1992, The Center for Substance Abuse Treatment was created to expand the availability and quality of addiction treatment. The Americans With Disabilities Acts extended job protection (except in safety sensitive positions) to alcoholics and recovering drug addicts in the private sector.

In 1993 President Clinton included a treatment benefit for alcoholism and other drug addictions in his national health care reform proposal. In 1995 the U.S. Supreme Court upheld the right of public schools to test student athletes for drug use. The U.S. Food and Drug Administration approved prescription use of naltrexone in treatment for alcoholism. Naltrexone marks the emergence of a new generation of pharmacological adjuncts in the treatment of alcoholism and other addictions. In 1998 the Center for Substance Abuse Treatment began funding local/regional Recovery Community Support Projects whose primary purposes are recovery advocacy.

(Primary Source: White, W. (1998). Slaying the Dragon: The History of Addiction Treatment and Recovery in America. Bloomington, IL: Chestnut Health Systems. 2000)

Chapter Three:
The Effects of Alcohol

ALCOHOL'S EFFECTS ON THE BRAIN

Effects on the brain include difficulty walking, blurred vision, slurred speech, slowed reaction times, impaired memory: Clearly, alcohol affects the brain. Some of these impairments are detectable after only one or two drinks and quickly resolve when drinking stops. On the other hand, a person who drinks heavily over a long period of time may have brain deficits that persist well after he or she achieves sobriety. Exactly how alcohol affects the brain and the likelihood of reversing the impact of heavy drinking on the brain remain hot topics in alcohol research today.

We do know that heavy drinking may have extensive and far–reaching effects on the brain, ranging from simple "slips" in memory to permanent and debilitating conditions that require lifetime custodial care. And even moderate drinking leads to short–term impairment, as shown by extensive research on the impact of drinking on driving.

A number of factors influence how and to what extent alcohol affects the brain, including

- how much and how often a person drinks;
- the age at which he or she first began drinking, and how long he or she has been drinking;
- the person's age, level of education, gender, genetic background, and family history of alcoholism;

- whether he or she is at risk as a result of prenatal alcohol exposure; and
- his or her general health status.

This chapter reviews some common disorders associated with alcohol–related brain damage and the people at greatest risk for impairment.

BLACKOUTS AND MEMORY LAPSES

Alcohol can produce detectable impairments in memory after only a few drinks and, as the amount of alcohol increases, so does the degree of impairment. Large quantities of alcohol, especially when consumed quickly and on an empty stomach, can produce a blackout, or an interval of time for which the intoxicated person cannot recall key details of events, or even entire events.

Blackouts are much more common among social drinkers than previously assumed and should be viewed as a potential consequence of acute intoxication regardless of age or whether the drinker is clinically dependent on alcohol. White and colleagues surveyed 772 college undergraduates about their experiences with blackouts and asked, "Have you ever awoken after a night of drinking not able to remember things that you did or places that you went?" Of the students who had ever consumed alcohol, 51 percent reported blacking out at some point in their lives, and 40 percent reported experiencing a blackout in the year before the survey. Of those who reported drinking in the 2 weeks before the survey, 9.4 percent said they blacked out during that time. The students reported learning later that they had participated in a wide range of potentially dangerous events they could not remember, including vandalism, unprotected sex, and driving.

Equal numbers of men and women reported experiencing blackouts, despite the fact that the men drank significantly more often and more heavily than the women. This outcome suggests that regardless of the amount of alcohol consumption, females—a group infrequently studied in the literature on blackouts—are at greater risk than males for experiencing blackouts. A woman's tendency to black out more easily probably results from differences in how men and women metabolize alcohol. Females also may be more susceptible than males to milder forms of alcohol–induced memory impairments, even when men and women consume comparable amounts of alcohol.

Women are more vulnerable than men to many of the medical consequences of alcohol use. For example, alcoholic women develop cirrhosis, alcohol–induced damage of the heart muscle (i.e., cardiomyopathy), and nerve damage (i.e., peripheral neuropathy) after fewer years of heavy drinking than do alcoholic men. Studies comparing men and women's sensitivity to alcohol–induced brain damage, however, have not been as conclusive.

Using imaging with computerized tomography, two studies compared brain shrinkage, a common indicator of brain damage, in alcoholic men and women and reported that male and female alcoholics both showed significantly greater brain shrinkage than control subjects. Studies also showed that both men and women have similar learning and memory problems as a result of heavy drinking. The difference is that alcoholic women reported that they had been drinking excessively for only about half as long as the alcoholic men in these studies. This indicates that women's brains, like their other organs, are more vulnerable to alcohol–induced damage than men's.

Yet other studies have not shown such definitive findings. In fact, two reports appearing side by side in the *American Journal of Psychiatry* contradicted each other on the question of gender–related vulnerability to brain shrinkage in alcoholism. Clearly, more research is needed on this topic, especially because alcoholic women have received less research attention than alcoholic men despite good evidence that women may be particularly vulnerable to alcohol's effects on many key organ systems.

People who have been drinking large amounts of alcohol for long periods of time run the risk of developing serious and persistent changes in the brain. Damage may be a result of the direct effects of alcohol on the brain or may result indirectly, from a poor general health status or from severe liver disease.

For example, thiamine deficiency is a common occurrence in people with alcoholism and results from poor overall nutrition. Thiamine, also known as vitamin B1, is an essential nutrient required by all tissues, including the brain. Thiamine is found in foods such as meat and poultry; whole grain cereals; nuts; and dried beans, peas, and soybeans. Many foods in the United States commonly are fortified with thiamine, including breads and cereals. As a result, most people consume sufficient amounts of thiamine in their diets. The typical intake for most Americans is 2 mg/day; the Recommended Daily Allowance is 1.2 mg/day for men and 1.1 mg/day for women.

Up to 80 percent of alcoholics, however, have a deficiency in thiamine, and some of these people will go on to develop serious brain disorders such as Wernicke–Korsakoff syndrome (WKS). WKS is a disease that consists of two separate syndromes, a short–lived and severe condition called Wernicke's encephalopathy and a long–lasting and debilitating condition known as Korsakoff's psychosis.

The symptoms of Wernicke's encephalopathy include mental confusion, paralysis of the nerves that move the eyes (i.e., oculomotor disturbances), and difficulty with muscle coordination. For example, patients with Wernicke's encephalopathy may be too confused to find their way out of a room or may not even be able to walk. Many Wernicke's encephalopathy patients, however, do not exhibit all three of these signs and symptoms, and clinicians working with alcoholics must be aware that this disorder may be present even if the patient shows only one or two of them. In fact, studies performed after death indicate that many cases of thiamine deficiency–related encephalopathy may not be diagnosed in life because not all the "classic" signs and symptoms were present or recognized.

Approximately 80 to 90 percent of alcoholics with Wernicke's encephalopathy also develop

Korsakoff's psychosis, a chronic and debilitating syndrome characterized by persistent learning and memory problems. Patients with Korsakoff's psychosis are forgetful and quickly frustrated and have difficulty with walking and coordination. Although these patients have problems remembering old information (i.e., retrograde amnesia), it is their difficulty in "laying down" new information (i.e., anterograde amnesia) that is the most striking. For example, these patients can discuss in detail an event in their lives, but an hour later might not remember ever having the conversation.

The cerebellum, an area of the brain responsible for coordinating movement and perhaps even some forms of learning, appears to be particularly sensitive to the effects of thiamine deficiency and is the region most frequently damaged in association with chronic alcohol consumption. Administering thiamine helps to improve brain function, especially in patients in the early stages of WKS. When damage to the brain is more severe, the course of care shifts from treatment to providing support to the patient and his or her family. Custodial care may be necessary for the 25 percent of patients who have permanent brain damage and significant loss of cognitive skills.

Scientists believe that a genetic variation could be one explanation for why only some alcoholics with thiamine deficiency go on to develop severe conditions such as WKS, but additional studies are necessary to clarify how genetic variants might cause some people to be more vulnerable to WKS than others.

Most people realize that heavy, long–term drinking can damage the liver, the organ chiefly responsible for breaking down alcohol into harmless byproducts and clearing it from the body. But people may not be aware that prolonged liver dysfunction, such as liver cirrhosis resulting from excessive alcohol consumption, can harm the brain, leading to a serious and potentially fatal brain disorder known as hepatic encephalopathy.

Hepatic encephalopathy can cause changes in sleep patterns, mood, and personality; psychiatric conditions such as anxiety and depression; severe cognitive effects such as shortened attention span; and problems with coordination such as a flapping or shaking of the hands (called asterixis). In the most serious cases, patients may slip into a coma (i.e., hepatic coma), which can be fatal.

New imaging techniques have enabled researchers to study specific brain regions in patients with alcoholic liver disease, giving them a better understanding of how hepatic encephalopathy develops. These studies have confirmed that at least two toxic substances, ammonia and manganese, have a role in the development of hepatic encephalopathy. Alcohol–damaged liver cells allow excess amounts of these harmful byproducts to enter the brain, thus harming brain cells.

Physicians typically use the following strategies to prevent or treat the development of hepatic encephalopathy.

- Treatment that lowers blood ammonia concentrations, such as administering L–ornithine L–aspartate.

- Techniques such as liver–assist devices, or "artificial livers," that clear the patients' blood of harmful toxins. In initial studies, patients using these devices showed lower amounts of ammonia circulating in their blood, and their encephalopathy became less severe.

- Liver transplantation, an approach that is widely used in alcoholic cirrhotic patients with severe (i.e., end–stage) chronic liver failure. In general, implantation of a new liver results in significant improvements in cognitive function in these patients and lowers their levels of ammonia and manganese.

Drinking during pregnancy can lead to a range of physical, learning, and behavioral effects in the developing brain, the most serious of which is a collection of symptoms known as fetal alcohol syndrome (FAS). Children with FAS may have distinct facial features (see illustration). FAS infants also are markedly smaller than average. Their brains may have less volume (i.e., microencephaly). And they may have fewer numbers of brain cells (i.e., neurons) or fewer neurons that are able to function correctly, leading to long–term problems in learning and behavior.

Scientists are investigating the use of complex motor training and medications to prevent or reverse the alcohol–related brain damage found in people prenatally exposed to alcohol. In a study using rats, Klintsova and colleagues used an obstacle course to teach complex motor skills, and this skills training led to a re–organization in the adult rats' brains (i.e., cerebellum), enabling them to overcome the effects of the prenatal alcohol exposure. These findings have important therapeutic implications, suggesting that complex rehabilitative motor training can improve motor performance of children, or even adults, with FAS.

Scientists also are looking at the possibility of developing medications that can help alleviate or prevent brain damage, such as that associated with FAS. Studies using animals have yielded encouraging results for treatments using antioxidant therapy and vitamin E. Other preventive therapies showing promise in animal studies include 1–octanol, which ironically is an alcohol itself. Treatment with 1–octanol significantly reduced the severity of alcohol's effects on developing mouse embryos. Two molecules associated with normal development (i.e., NAP and SAL) have been found to protect nerve cells against a variety of toxins in much the same way that octanol does. And a compound (MK–801) that blocks a key brain chemical associated with alcohol withdrawal (i.e., glutamate) also is being studied. MK–801 reversed a specific learning impairment that resulted from early postnatal alcohol exposure.

Though these compounds were effective in animals, the positive results cited here may or may not translate to humans. Not drinking during pregnancy is the best form of prevention; FAS remains the leading *preventable* birth defect in the United States today.

For decades scientists believed that the number of nerve cells in the adult brain was fixed early in life. If brain damage occurred, then, the best way to treat it was by strengthening the existing neurons, as new ones could not be added. In the 1960s, however, researchers found that new neurons are indeed generated in adulthood—a process called neurogenesis. These new cells originate from stem cells, which are cells that can divide indefinitely, renew themselves, and give rise to a variety of cell types. The discovery of brain stem cells and adult neurogenesis provides a new way of approaching the problem of alcohol–related changes in the brain and may lead to a clearer understanding of how best to treat and cure alcoholism.

For example, studies with animals show that high doses of alcohol lead to a disruption in the growth of new brain cells; scientists believe it may be this lack of new growth that results in the long–term deficits found in key areas of the brain (such as hippocampal structure and function). Understanding how alcohol interacts with brain stem cells and what happens to these cells in alcoholics is the first step in establishing whether the use of stem cell therapies is an option for treatment.

Alcoholics are not all alike. They experience different degrees of impairment, and the disease has different origins for different people. Consequently, researchers have not found conclusive evidence that any one variable is solely responsible for the brain deficits found in alcoholics. Characterizing what makes some alcoholics vulnerable to brain damage whereas others are not remains the subject of active research.

The good news is that most alcoholics with cognitive impairment show at least some improvement in brain structure and functioning within a year of abstinence, though some people take much longer. Clinicians must consider a variety of treatment methods to help people stop drinking and to recover from alcohol–related brain impairments, and tailor these treatments to the individual patient.

Advanced technology will have an important role in developing these therapies. Clinicians can use brain–imaging techniques to monitor the course and success of treatment, because imaging can reveal structural, functional, and biochemical changes in living patients over time. Promising new medications also are in the early stages of development, as researchers strive to design therapies that can help prevent alcohol's harmful effects and promote the growth of new brain cells to take the place of those that have been damaged by alcohol.

(From the National Institute of Alcohol and Alcoholism)

Part Two

Treating Alcohol Use Disorders

Chapter Four:
Special Challenges

In the past 40 years or so there has been a tendency to blend treatment of alcohol use disorders into the general field of treatment of substance use disorders. In many ways this makes sense as the same tools and techniques are used no matter the substance that the person is abusing. There are some particular challenges, however, that one finds in treating alcohol use disorders.

One challenge is that withdrawal from alcohol is potentially fatal. Alcohol has a depressive effect on the system. It slows down brain function and changes the way nerves send messages back and forth.

Over time, the central nervous system adjusts to having alcohol around all the time. The body works hard to keep the brain in a more awake state and to keep nerves talking to one another.

When the alcohol level suddenly drops, the brain stays in this keyed up state. That's what causes withdrawal.

Withdrawal symptoms can range from mild to serious. What they are depends on how much one drank and for how long. Mild symptoms usually show up as early as 6 hours after one stops drinking. They can include anxiety, shaky hands, headache, nausea, vomiting, insomnia, and sweating.

More serious problems can occur, and range from hallucinations about 12 to 24 hours after the last drink to seizures within the first 2 days after stopping. A person may see, feel, or hear things that aren't there.

That isn't the same as delirium tremens, or DTs as they are commonly called. DTs usually start 48 to 72 hours after the last drink. These are severe symptoms that include vivid hallucinations and delusions. Only about 5% of people with alcohol withdrawal have them. Those that do may also have: confusion, racing heart, high blood pressure, fever, and heavy sweating.

To diagnose possible withdrawal, the person will be asked questions about their drinking history and how recently they stopped. They'll also be asked if they have gone through withdrawal before. They'll also discuss the person's symptoms. During an exam, they'll look for other medical conditions to see if they could be to blame.

Alcohol withdrawal can be fatal. A medical detox is needed if the person shows any severe symptoms. There may be a wait before a detox bed becomes available. In cases like that the person may need to continue drinking until a space in a detox unit is available.

Another unique factor is alcohol use disorders is the fact that alcohol is not only legal but plays a major role in society. While cannabis is being legalized in many states, there is still a stigma attached to it from all the years it was considered a dangerous and illicit substance. Nicotine is legal, but the health risks that not only affect the user but can also affect those exposed to second-hand smoke have slowly begun to make that less socially accepted.

Alcohol, however, remains an accepted mood-altering substance. Use of alcohol to celebrate special occasions is prevalent in much of our society. Having a drink to relax and unwind is a common event. Alcohol is used in religious rituals. It is sold at numerous locations, including some grocery stores, convenience stores, and is served at many restaurants.

Even though alcohol can have debilitating health consequences, it isn't considered as dangerous as tobacco since there are no second-hand health effects. There are, of course, second-hand effects on the people around the person who has an alcohol use disorder, but society doesn't deem them as much a threat as second-hand smoke.

The social acceptability of alcohol can make recovery from alcohol use disorder difficult. Those around the person in recovery are more likely to see the disorder as a weakness or moral failing since many who drink do not have a problem with drinking. The recovering person may be encouraged to "just have one to be sociable" since the person making this suggestion has no difficulty having only one drink. The social acceptability of alcohol also makes it harder for a person in recovery to avoid a situation that involves drinking since so many social situations in our society do involve consumption of alcohol.

Subsequent chapters of this book will refer generically to treatment of substance use disorders. Keep in mind that there is little difference in how these disorders are treated, but that there are these special challenges for those who have an alcohol use disorder.

Chapter Five
Basic Views of Addiction

In order to treat addiction, one must first have an understanding of the development, progression, and effects of addiction. As in most areas of psychology, there are many theories of addiction. The theory that a clinician accepts will affect the type of treatment that is given. There are several major theories that are predominant in the field of addiction treatment.

At the heart of theories of addiction are basic views of addiction. Thombs (1994) outlines three basic views: addiction as sin, as a disease, and as maladaptive behavior. The first view, addiction as sin, is the oldest view. It considers the addictive use of alcohol or other drugs as a moral weakness. This view implies that the person makes a conscious choice to use these substances to excess. While this view is not as openly embraced as it used to be, it still has its supporters, especially in the legal and law-enforcement fields.

The second view is addiction as a disease. This view is the basis for a lot of addiction treatment in the United States. This view has been around since the 18th century but gained support and influence in the years following the end of prohibition. Prohibition was based on the assumption that alcohol was "evil." The prohibitionists believed that anyone who drank alcohol was likely to become an alcoholic. When prohibition was repealed there was a need to justify the legal sale of alcohol (Pita, 1998). The disease concept suggested that alcohol was not the problem; the problem was a genetic flaw in a small percentage of the population. The most widely accepted definition of the disease of addiction is:

A chronic, primary, hereditary, eventually fatal disease that progresses from an early physiological susceptibility into an addiction characterized by tolerance changes, physiological dependence, and loss of control over drinking (Mueller & Ketcham, 1987).

While this particular definition was given specifically to cover alcohol addiction, it has been applied to any form of chemical dependency. Accordingly, the Chronic Disease Model is based on the belief that addictive disease is primarily a biochemical/genetic disorder that is activated by the use of the drug.

The third view of addiction is that of addiction as maladaptive behavior. This view suggests that addiction is neither a moral failing nor a biochemical disease. Addiction is considered to be neither sinful nor out of control. It is seen as a behavior problem that is under the control of environment, family, social, and/or cognitive contingencies (Thombs, 1994). The exact nature of the cause and treatment in this view is often dependent on the school of psychological thought that the therapist subscribes to.

While I do not find direct medical evidence that would identify addiction as a disease, I feel that it is a reasonable way to describe a multi-faceted problem. I choose this view for several reasons. First, it is the standard view in the field; it is easier to work with this view than against it. Also, a disease concept recognizes the physical aspects of substance dependence. I find myself, however, at odds with Mueller and Ketcham's Chronic Disease definition.

The April, 2001 issue of *Counselor: The Magazine for Addiction Professionals* includes an article by William White, titled, "A Disease Concept for the 21st Century." Since the understanding of the Disease model of addiction presented in this article echoes my own; I will review the basics of the model presented in that article.

White suggests, first of all, that there is a need for a new definition of disease. He notes that the medical field is moving away from viewing disease as an entity toward understanding disease as a metaphor; disease is a word and idea used to convey "substantial, deteriorating changes in the structure and function of the human body and the accompanying deterioration in biopsychosocial functioning" (White, 2001). I feel this is an excellent definition that is appropriate to describe addiction. White also states that this model must be clear in defining the conditions and circumstances to which it is applied. He warns against applying it to "process addictions" such as harmful relationships to food, sex, work, and gambling.

White also suggests that alcoholism/addiction must be placed within a larger context of alcohol and other drug (AOD) problems. He points out that there are levels of AOD related problems, and that each level requires different intervention strategies. White states, "If the field continues to rely solely on a narrowly prescribed addiction intervention model, then ethically it must refuse to treat the wider pool of individuals with AOD problems for whom this model is inappropriate and potentially harmful (White, 2001)."

Who is appropriate for addiction treatment? The *Diagnostic and Statistical Manual of Mental Disorders, Fifth Edition,* commonly referred to as the *DSM-V*, offers diagnostic tools that identify Substance Use Disorder. This is determined by the presence of three or more of the following, occurring within a twelve-month period:

1) Recurrent substance use resulting in a failure to fulfill major role obligations at work, school or home.

2) Recurrent substance use in situations in which it is physically hazardous

3) Continued substance use despite having persistent or recurrent social or inter-personal problems caused or exacerbated by the effects of the substance

4) Tolerance, as defined by either of the following:

a) A need for markedly increased amounts of the substance to achieve the desired effect

b) Markedly diminished effect with continued use of the same amount of the substance

5) Withdrawal, as manifested by either of the following:

a) The characteristic withdrawal syndrome for the substance

b) The same (or a closely related) substance is taken to relieve or avoid withdrawal symptoms

6)   The substance is often taken in larger amounts or over a longer period than was intended

7)   There is a persistent desire or unsuccessful efforts to cut down or control substance use

8)   A great deal of time is spent in activities necessary to obtain the substance, to use the substance, or to recover from its effects

9)   Important social, occupational, or recreational activities are given up or reduced because of the substance use

10)   The substance is used despite knowledge of having a persistent or recurrent physical or psychological problem that is likely to have been caused or exacerbated by the substance

11)   Craving or a strong desire or urge to use a specific substance

(APA, 2013).

In this model, a person's level of need for treatment is determined according to a continuum of severity of the disorder. A person meeting 2–3 criteria would indicate a mild disorder; 4–5 criteria, a moderate disorder; and 6 or more, a severe disorder. The severity of the disorder should indicate the level of treatment needed.

Another important concept in White's approach is a concept that is also central to mine. He points out that the new disease concept will "celebrate the variety of styles and pathways of long-term recovery management" (White, 2001). In other words, the addictions field must recognize that there can be, and should be, a variety of ways to resolve AOD problems. Rather than offering "*the* program," addiction professionals should offer a menu of options that fit the individual personally and culturally.

White also states that addiction should be portrayed as "a cluster of disorders that spring from multiple interacting etiological influences and that vary considerably in their onset, course, and outcome (White, 2001). White further states that the new disease concept will state within its framework that:

1) Addiction is not caused solely by genetic or biological factors but by multiple interacting factors, a status that places it squarely within the rubric of other chronic diseases,

2) Not all addictions are progressive (accelerating), some remain stable but enduring while others decelerate, just like many other chronic diseases,

3) Patterns of spontaneous remission and maturing out exist in addiction just as they do with many other chronic diseases, and

4) The movement from an AOD problem to a level of continued alcohol and drug use below the priming dose of problem activation is common in those with transient AOD problems, but rare in those with patterns of severe and persistent addiction (White, 2001).

Based on this disease model, it is my belief that there are three areas of the person's life that are affected by addiction. An easy way to identify and remember these areas is by referring to them as PTA: physical, thinking (cognition), and action (behavior). Effective treatment will address all three areas.

In order to understand the physical aspect of addiction, one must look at the physical effects of drugs and alcohol. Any mood-altering substance creates its effect by changing brain chemistry. Therefore, it is important to understand the basics of the way the brain functions to understand how drugs affect the brain. This is not an in-depth study, but is intended to give a rudimentary understanding of brain function. The information on brain chemistry can be very difficult to understand. *Buzzed*, by Kuhn, Swartzwelder, & Wilson (1998), offers an easily understood explanation of brain function. The information that follows comes primarily from that source.

The first step is to understand neurons, which have been called the building blocks of the central nervous system. Neurons have three basic areas. The top receiving areas are called dendrites. This is where connections from other neurons make contact. Next is the "trunk" area, which contains the genetic information of the cell. Last is the axon of the cell, which is similar to tree roots, these make contact with other cells and transmit signals to them. The point of contact between the axon of one neuron and the dendrite of another is the synapse. Each terminal contains chemicals, called neurotransmitters. These act as chemical signals to activate or inhibit the function of neighboring cells. These are released into the space between the axon of one cell and the dendrite of another. Each neurotransmitter reacts with receptors that are sensitive to that particular chemical. A single neuron can have millions of synapses on its dendrites, and the cell body takes in signals from all those synapses. It then decides whether to fire electrical signals itself.

This information is important in understanding addiction, as different drugs affect different receptors. Benzodiazepines, which are minor tranquilizers, for example, bind with GABA receptor sites. Alcohol, another depressant, does not act with a specific receptor site; it produces a general increase in the fluidity of membranes. LSD, a hallucinogenic drug, reacts with the two major groups of serotonin receptors; it blocks one while it excites the other. Opiates act by binding to receptor sites for the endorphin/encephalin class of neurotransmitters.

Since there is a physical aspect of substance addiction, there may be a need to use medications as part of the treatment process. In the October 3, 1997 issue of the journal, *Science*, Charles P. O'Brien points out that many psychiatric disorders commonly coexist with addictive disorders. While many will debate whether the addiction brought on the coexisting disorder, or if the disorder brought on the addiction, it is clear that both disorders need to be treated. This would include the standard cognitive, behavioral, and educational interventions for the addiction as well as appropriate medications and therapy for the psychological disorder. I have seen many clients who, for various reasons, refuse to use medications for depression or bipolar disorders. In most of these cases, the person is not successful in maintaining abstinence from drugs; the chemical imbalance prevents them from making lasting changes in their drug use. On the other hand, I have also seen patients decline treatment for their addiction; these people feel that treating the chemical imbalance will correct the problem. In many cases, these people return within months for a new assessment for addiction treatment.

Another area in which medical intervention seems to be indicated is in the treatment of opiate addiction. The relapse rate for people with opiate addiction is quite high. One reason for this is the intense physical effects that a person experiences when withdrawing from opiates. Mild withdrawal symptoms from opiates occur as soon as the last dose of the medication wears off. Early opiate withdrawal symptoms include watery eyes, runny nose, yawning, and sweating. Later symptoms include restlessness, irritability, and loss of appetite, diarrhea, shivering, sweating, abdominal cramps, muscle pains, and increased sensitivity to pain. The worst of these symptoms abate after a few days.

The desire to avoid these symptoms is one factor that leads a person to continue opiate use long after the use becomes an impediment. The obvious answer would be to medicate the person during the detoxification period to ease the effects of withdrawal, and then begin a drug-free treatment regimen. While this works for some people, there are many others who are not successful with this approach. For those who do not do well with detox and drug-free treatment, there is a valid option. That option is Medication Assisted Treatment.

Since addiction has cognitive and behavioral as well as physical effects, there is a need to provide assistance to clients that will address these areas. There are several leading theories of addiction treatment that influence the view presented in this book; I will present brief views of them here. These views are not meant to fully represent the theory and will, by their brevity, simplify and possibly misrepresent the theory. Any interest in these theories should be more fully satisfied by going to the original source of the theory.

As stated earlier, the disease view of addiction is the basis for most addiction treatment in the United States. Thombs (1994) actually lists the Disease Model as a theory of addiction in addition to being a view of addiction. He points out that the disease model has helped to lessen the stigma against people with addiction problems. The basis of this model, as stated earlier, is the belief that addiction is a biochemical and/or genetic disorder. Thombs points out that there are, in reality, several concepts of what the disease of addiction may be. The disease model of Alcoholics Anonymous (AA) stresses the importance of spirituality in the etiology, and recovery from, alcoholism; many people in AA state that they are recovering from a "spiritual disease" (Thombs, 1994). In the medical community, there is a focus on the significance of biological factors that affect addiction.

The method of treatment under the disease model is more closely aligned with AA's understanding of disease rather than with that of the medical community. Participation in twelve-step support groups such as AA or Narcotics Anonymous (NA) is usually mandatory. Those in treatment are commonly referred to as patients rather than clients. Since the disease model states that addiction is a primary disease, meaning that it is not the result of another condition, there is no attempt to look at underlying factors that may have influenced the person's pattern of drug or alcohol use. Patients are encouraged to "work the steps": admitting they are powerless over the drug, that a "Greater Power" could "restore them to sanity," and that they should turn their lives over to this Higher Power.

It is interesting to note that aspects of other treatment approaches are finding their way into AA based treatment. Aspects of Reality, Behavioral, and Cognitive Therapies are being incorporated into most treatment programs at this time. The basis of the treatment, however, remains the Twelve Steps of AA and a "spiritual awakening." It should also be noted that medical interventions are rare in this model. While the use of medicine during a "detox" period, to lessen the severity of withdrawal symptoms, is accepted practice, the use of drugs such as Methadone to treat opiate addiction is highly criticized by many people in the treatment field. Some AA hard-liners even object to the use of medically prescribed antidepressants.

Most of the other theories of addiction are rooted in psychology. As a result, they fall under the view of addiction as maladaptive behavior. These approaches are based on personality theories developed by various leaders in psychological thought. As noted earlier, the disease model rejects the notion that addiction can be the result of anything but a biochemical/genetic problem, yet many of the treatment approaches developed by these theorists have been incorporated into conventional treatment.

Perhaps the most controversial approach, at least as far as the disease model community is concerned, is the Psychoanalytical approach. This is based on many of Freud's concepts of the unconscious, ego development, free association, the seeking of pleasure (ego gratification), and disruption of stages of development. This treatment method relies on long-term individual sessions with a psychoanalyst. The object is to help a person realize the unconscious problems that cause them to rely on alcohol and drugs. This approach, obviously, is in direct conflict with the notion that addiction is a primary disease without underlying causes. It is ironic that one of the central points of the disease model, denial as a defense mechanism, is firmly rooted in Freudian theory.

Another theory of addiction is Conditioning Theory, based on aspects of Behavioral psychology. Behavioral psychology limits itself to the study of observable behaviors and is not interested in "mental" constructs such as self-esteem, affective states, thoughts, and values. The most prominent Behaviorist, B.F. Skinner, believed that individuals did not choose to become addicted to chemicals; he believed that they are conditioned to engage in frequent drug-taking behavior by a "society that is afraid to implement a scientific technology of behavior" (Thombs, 1994). Behaviorists recognize two types of conditioned behaviors. Respondent conditioning is reflexive; an example would be blinking in response to a bright light. Operant conditioning is considered to be voluntary; an operant behavior is conditioned if a reinforcer follows it. Alcohol and drugs are seen as potentially powerful reinforcers.

A Behavioral definition of addiction is "an operantly conditioned response whose tendency becomes stronger as a function of the quality, number, and size of reinforcements that follows each drug ingestion (Thombs, 1994)." In alcohol and drug use there are three classes of reinforcers: euphoria, social variables, and elimination of withdrawal sickness. Behavioral treatment for addiction would consist of behavior modification techniques. Assuming that alcohol and drug use and addiction are learned behaviors, the counselor's role is to assist clients in learning more effective ways of behaving to reach their goals.

Another theory of addiction is based on Social Learning Theory. This view suggests that humans can create and administer reinforcements for themselves and to themselves. This view suggests that internal cognitive processes influence behaviors. It states that cognitive processes are based on prior experience and serve to determine the following: (1) which environmental influences are attended to, (2) how these influences are perceived (for example as "good" or "bad"), (3) whether they will be remembered, and (4) how they may affect future behavior (Thombs, 1994).

It is under this theory that the cognitive/behavioral approach, especially as presented by Albert Ellis, enters addiction treatment. Stated plainly, Ellis believes that a person does not react to an event, but rather to what they *believe* about that event. This philosophy is easily understood in the following example: A group of students entering a classroom are told that they will have a pop quiz. Some students will react with feelings of anger, fear, and/or anxiety while others may react very calmly and may even feel happy about taking the quiz. The event is the same for all students; the difference lies in how they perceive it. Those students who are familiar with the material will feel confident while those who have not kept up with the reading will feel anxious.

I will explore the cognitive/behavioral approach and its application to addiction treatment, including an exploration of the controversy between it and AA, more fully in a later chapter. For now, I will state that this approach has become more accepted within traditional addiction treatment. Hazelden, a publisher long associated with the twelve-step and disease models of addiction, now offers booklets outlining the use of Ellis' Rational Emotive Behavior Therapy (REBT).

Reality Therapy is another approach that falls under the umbrella of Social Learning Theory. Reality Therapy rejects the concept of "mental illness" and suggests that emotional problems arise because people are unable to satisfy their needs realistically and they behave irresponsibly because they deny the reality of the world around them. Like Ellis' REBT, the focus is not on the patient's past, but on the present and future. The therapist has the task of teaching his clients to acquire the ability to fulfill their needs in a way that does not deprive others of the ability to fulfill their needs (Glasser, 1965).

In addictions counseling, this approach helps the client to accept the reality that alcohol and drug use does not protect them from problems, and, in fact, creates more problems. The counselor helps clients find new ways to cope with problems. Reality Therapy and REBT work well with the disease model, as they do not focus on the client's past, instead offering ways to change present behavior.

Family Systems Theory offers another approach to addiction treatment. It suggests that families are guided by rules, which are often unspoken but are known to the family, and by relationship patterns. If one element in the system is changed, the entire system attempts to compensate for the change. As in Social Learning Theory, psychological factors are not usually considered.

As applied to addiction, Family Systems Theory suggests that the chemical use of a family member affects the rules and relationships within the family. It is suggested that there are three basic rules in these families: (1) do not talk about the addiction, (2) do not confront the addictive behavior, and, (3) protect and shelter the addicted person so things do not become worse (Thombs,

1994). These rules, of course, enable the addicted person to continue in their addiction, which can lead to progression of the addiction. If the addicted person should stop their addiction, the family balance is disturbed. Family Systems Theory suggests that the addicted person may areturn to active use to restore the balance; often under direct or indirect pressure from family members. Therefore, treatment for addiction should include, to some degree or other, the entire family. At the very least, the person in treatment needs to be aware of the possible changes within the family and must be prepared to cope with them.

A theory that is becoming more popular in treating addiction is that of Motivational Interviewing (MI). This model is based on the Stages of Change, and provides techniques to engage the client and to help them move to the Action stage. I will talk more about this in a later chapter

These theories and views, along with practical experience, have led me to develop an approach to addiction treatment that draws from a variety of sources. This approach, which I call Positive Path Recovery, is designed to be either a complementary alternative to twelve-step based treatment, or an adjunct to it. I call this approach Positive Path Recovery for several reasons. First, the client is encouraged to have a positive attitude toward recovery. Rather that thinking that they must "give up" drug use, they believe that they are building a healthier, more productive life. A positive view of recovery and treatment allows the client to become more invested in that process.

Positive Path Recovery also encourages the client to have a positive self-image. Poor self-esteem is a frequent effect of, if not an influence upon, drug and alcohol addiction. Clients are encouraged to have a positive self-image while acknowledging the negative effects of their drug use.

Clients are encouraged to have a positive attitude toward others as well. While some of the beliefs that supported the person's drug use may have come from friends and family, the client is urged to avoid placing blame on others. The client also needs to recognize that others may not respond to them in the manner that they would prefer. The restoration of trust can be slow, and forgiveness for past actions may also be slow or may never be given. The client needs to try to understand how the other person feels, and to accept that he or she cannot blame that person for those feelings.

Positive Path Recovery allows the client and counselor to work as a team to develop an individualized plan to meet the client's needs. It is, after all, the client's life, and they should be able to have a say in their treatment plan.

Chapter Six:
Motivating Change

In an ideal world, everyone who comes for treatment would come with an understanding of their problem and a deep-felt determination to change. In fact, many, if not most, of the people I have seen for treatment come under some type of compulsion. The reason may be legal problems, or family pressure, some type of employment problems, or some other outside force that has the person presenting for treatment before they have determined the need for treatment. In treatment, it is quite common for the person to decide that they want to control addiction to one substance but not be committed to abstinence from all mood-altering drugs. While this does not mean that treatment is impossible, it does make it difficult.

If a client who enters our office does not feel he or she has a problem, it may be difficult to get them to fully engage; without engagement, change will not come about. Our first job, therefore, is to work with that person in a way that might help them come to their own decision to make changes in their life.

It is important for a clinician to recognize the process and stages of change. It is here that an understanding of the Stages of Change model and learning about the various Motivational Interviewing and Motivational Enhancement Therapy techniques becomes necessary.

In 1986, Prochaska and DiClemente developed the Stages of Change model. They identified five stages of change:

Pre-contemplation is the stage where the person is not yet convinced there is a problem or a need for change. A person who enters treatment at this phase is generally doing so under compulsion. As stated earlier, many of the clients I have seen over the years have entered treatment at this stage. The clinician's job at this point is to help the client recognize that they need to commit to recovery.

Contemplation is the stage where the person becomes aware that a problem exists and begins to think about doing something about it. Again, if a service recipient enters treatment at this stage, it is generally due to outside pressure. The clinician still needs to work with the client to engage them in treatment.

Preparation is a stage where a person is poised for action; they may even begin to make some attempt at change on their own. The person might even make the first move toward starting treatment, even thought they are not totally convinced that they are ready to do this.

The *Action* stage is where the major change occurs. The person is committed to change and begins to do the work required for lasting recovery. This stage can take time, work, and energy. It is at this stage when the person has fully admitted the problem and makes a commitment to change. *Maintenance*, the fifth stage, is not a part of this discussion; it will be looked at in a later chapter.

The challenge of the clinician in most cases is to work with the client to help them move toward the Action stage. This can be accomplished in many ways; some ways, however, have been proven to more effective than others.

In the August 2007 issue of *Counselor: The Magazine for Addiction Professionals,* William White and William Miller discuss the use of confrontation in addiction treatment. In the past, beginning around the 1920's and going on through the 1970's, confrontational therapy was widely used in addiction treatment. This approach was based on a theory that addicted people had defense mechanisms that were more highly developed than non-addicted people. The belief was that the job of the addiction professional was to "Break 'em down to build 'em back up" (White and Miller, 2007). A series of clinical studies have since shown that harsh, confrontational approaches are not any more effective than other approaches. It is now believed that these approaches actually help to build and strengthen defense mechanisms, such as denial. Despite these findings, there are still a number of professionals in the addiction treatment field who rely on confrontational approaches.

I remember a time when I was asked to confront a client about a positive urine drug screen. My supervisor was trained during the days when harsh confrontational counseling was considered the best (perhaps only) way to help people with addiction; I am sure he felt I was too soft and could not be effective. I called the person into my office and stated that the recent screen was positive. She immediately denied using. I explained that I was not looking to get her into trouble and was not planning to discharge her from treatment; I merely wanted to know how she was doing so I could better help her. She still denied drug use. I then calmly pointed out that she had given the sample and had verified that the sample was hers. I asked her, if she had not used drugs, how she felt the drugs had gotten into the sample. She hesitated for a moment, and then finally admitted that she had used cocaine due to having a headache. After pointing out to her that most people would have used aspirin, I then helped her to plan how she could prevent this from happening again. As it turned out, that was her last drug use during treatment; to my knowledge, she is still maintaining her recovery several years later.

I had, in fact, confronted this client. I just did not use the usual confrontation style that has been popular in addiction treatment. What I did was more along the lines of Motivational Interviewing. This is an approach to addiction treatment that is gaining popularity; one reason for this increased popularity is that it has been proven effective in many clinical trials.

Motivational Interviewing (MI), developed by Stephen Rollnick and William R. Miller, is a client-centered, directive method for enhancing intrinsic motivation to change by exploring and resolving ambivalence. The following information, from the official Motivational Interviewing website, offers an interesting look at this approach.

We believe it is vital to distinguish between the *spirit* of motivational interviewing and *techniques* that we have recommended to manifest that spirit. Clinicians and trainers who become too focused on matters of technique can lose sight of the spirit and style that are central to the approach. There are as many variations in technique as there are clinical encounters. The spirit of the method, however, is more enduring and can be characterized in a few key points.
Motivation to change is elicited from the client, and not imposed from without. Other motivational approaches have emphasized coercion, persuasion, constructive confrontation, and the use of external contingencies (e.g., the threatened loss of job or family). Such strategies may have their place in evoking change, but they are quite different in spirit from motivational interviewing which relies

upon identifying and mobilizing the client's intrinsic values and goals to stimulate behavior change.

1. *It is the client's task, not the counselor's, to articulate and resolve his or her ambivalence.* Ambivalence takes the form of a conflict between two courses of action (e.g., indulgence versus restraint), each of which has perceived benefits and costs associated with it. Many clients have never had the opportunity of expressing the often confusing, contradictory and uniquely personal elements of this conflict, for example, "If I stop smoking I will feel better about myself, but I may also put on weight, which will make me feel unhappy and unattractive." The counselor's task is to facilitate expression of both sides of the ambivalence impasse, and guide the client toward an acceptable resolution that triggers change.
2. *Direct persuasion is not an effective method for resolving ambivalence.* It is tempting to try to be "helpful" by persuading the client of the urgency of the problem about the benefits of change. It is fairly clear, however, that these tactics generally increase client resistance and diminish the probability of change (Miller, Benefield and Tonigan, 1993, Miller and Rollnick, 1991).

3. *The counseling style is generally a quiet and eliciting one.* Direct persuasion, aggressive confrontation, and argument-tation are the conceptual opposite of motivational interviewing and are explicitly proscribed in this approach. To a counselor accustomed to confronting and giving advice, motivational interviewing can appear to be a hopelessly slow and passive process. The proof is in the outcome. More aggressive strategies, sometimes guided by a desire to "confront client denial," easily slip into pushing clients to make changes for which they are not ready.

4. *The counselor is directive in helping the client to examine and resolve ambivalence.* Motivational interviewing involves no training of clients in behavioral coping skills, although the two approaches not incompatible. The operational assumption in motivational interviewing is that ambivalence or lack of resolve is the principal obstacle to be overcome in triggering change. Once that has been accomplished, there may or may not be a need for further intervention such as skill training. The specific strategies of motivational interviewing are designed to elicit, clarify, and resolve ambivalence in a client-centered and respectful counseling atmosphere.

5. *Readiness to change is not a client trait, but a fluctuating product of interpersonal interaction.* The therapist is therefore highly attentive and responsive to the client's motivational signs. Resistance and "denial" are seen not as client traits, but as feedback regarding therapist behavior. Client resistance is often a signal that the counselor is assuming greater readiness to change than is the case, and it is a cue that the therapist needs to modify motivational strategies.

6. *The therapeutic relationship is more like a partnership or companionship than expert/recipient roles.* The therapist respects the client's autonomy and freedom of choice (and consequences) regarding his or her own behavior.

Viewed in this way, it is inappropriate to think of motivational interviewing as a technique or set of techniques that are applied to or (worse) "used on" people. Rather, it is an interpersonal style, not at all restricted to formal counseling settings. It is a subtle balance of directive and client-centered components shaped by a guiding philosophy and understanding of what triggers change. If it becomes a trick or a manipulative technique, its essence has been lost (Miller, 1994).

With that having been said, there are techniques that are commonly used in Motivational Interviewing. I will give a brief overview of these here; I highly recommend that you visit the official Motivational Interviewing website to obtain detailed information. The web address is www.motivationalinterview.org.

The basic techniques of MI are found in the acronym *OARS:* **O**pen-ended questions, **A**ffirmations, **R**eflective listening, and **S**ummaries. I will briefly look at each of these techniques.

Open-ended questions are questions that cannot be answered by *yes* or *no*. A closed question allows a response but does not encourage further communication or exploration. "What brings you here today?" is a question that will result in a far different answer than asking, "Did you come because you think you have a problem?" Open-ended questions not only allow, but encourage openness and sharing.

Affirmations can help a client to feel fully accepted, capable to make change, and helps to build a sense of hope. Affirmations, however, must appear sincere. These affirmations are not simply general, positive statements; they are personal observations of the client's positive qualities and accomplishments.

Reflective listening is the key to this work. This is so important, that the following information is directly from the MI website as I couldn't word it better:

"The best motivational advice we can give you is to listen carefully to your clients. They will tell you what has worked and what hasn't. What moved them forward and shifted them backward. Whenever you are in doubt about what to do, listen. But remember this is a directive approach. Unlike Rogerian therapists, you will actively guide the client towards certain materials. You will focus on their change talk and provide less attention to non-change talk. For example, 'You are not quite sure you are ready to make a change, but you are quite aware that your drug use has caused concerns in your relationships, affected your work and that your doctor is worried about your health.

You will also want to vary your level of reflection. Keeping reflections at the surface level may lead to that feeling that the interaction is moving in circles. Reflections of affect, especially those that are unstated but likely, can be powerful motivators. For example, 'Your children aren't living with you anymore; that seems painful for you.' If you are right, the emotional intensity of the session deepens. If you are wrong or the client is unready to deal with this material, the client corrects you and the conversation moves forward.

The goal in MI is to create forward momentum and to then harness that momentum to create change. Reflective listening keeps that momentum moving forward. This is why the developers of MI recommend a ratio of three reflections for every question asked. Questions tend to cause a shift in momentum and can stop it entirely. Although there are times you will want to create a shift or stop momentum, most times you will want to keep it flowing."

Summaries are really another form of reflective listening. They help to recap what has been said and what insights have been gained. MI suggests doing them frequently so the amount of information to be summarized is not too overwhelming. Effective use of summaries allows important information to be repeated; this repetition helps people to retain the information.

The purpose of Motivational Interviewing is to help the client to commit to change. As discussed earlier in the chapter, while total abstinence is perhaps the best and ultimate goal, it may be necessary to move a client toward a goal of abstinence in stages. I have found that those clients who are mandated to treatment are especially reluctant to commit to a lifetime of abstinence. I have seen many people rebel against enforced abstinence to the point that they decide they would rather leave treatment and face the consequences than to stay in treatment being told what is right for them.

I have found it better to set short-term goals for people in these situations. I have told mandated clients, "The court says you have to complete this program in order to keep your license and stay out of jail. I can't tell you what to do with your life, but, you will come out for the better if you can stay away from alcohol and drugs for the next six months." I have had many people begin with that six-month commitment who have moved to a commitment for total abstinence before their treatment was complete.

When a client states he or she doesn't see the need to stay clean and sober, I try to help them to explore the ambivalence. I might say, "It sounds like you would rather face jail time or losing your license than to be told what to do. This must be important to you" That statement can sometimes help a person to see flaws in their thinking.

Making a commitment to a path of recovery may take time. The important thing is, however, that this commitment must come from the client. Our job is to help move the client toward that commitment.

Chapter Seven:
Self Awareness and Connection

As people become more deeply involved in the process of addiction, they lose connection with the basic sense of self. While they may believe that they have "self-control," it is actually the desire or need for the substance that is controlling them. In addiction, the person is *re*acting rather than acting. As a person begins the process of recovery, he or she needs to restore and strengthen the sense of self.

The topic of "self" is one of the basics of psychology. There are a variety of personality development theories; each theory of development leads to a theory of restoring a "disturbed" person to a healthy balance. Some theories are based on "nature;" they state that a person's personality is based on genetic influences. Other theories are "nurture" based, stating that environmental influences form the personality or self. There are some theories that suggest that personality is based on a third element, which is frequently defined as the "soul." Combining elements of these three approaches leads to what I feel is a workable theory of self as it applies to the process of addiction and recovery.

Perhaps the first task is to define the term, "self." In *Psychology of Adjustment* (Sawrey and Telford, 1971), the self is defined as having three aspects: the physical self, the social self, and the self-concept. The physical self is our first discovery as infants. It expands as our physical awareness of our bodies continues to evolve. As we become more aware of our environment, we develop the social self, which is the way we respond to others in our surroundings. "The child very early in life accepts as valid other people's judgments of him and his characteristics" (Sawrey and Telford,1971). These judgments help to build the self-concept. Unfortunately, for a number of people, these judgments are not always valid. Frequently, they are the sole basis of the self-concept.

This definition of self is, perhaps, compatible with many personality theories. It includes both nature and nurture. There is, however, an element that is missing. Sawrey and Telford state, "The self-concept is more important than the 'real self' in determining behavior" (Sawrey and Telford, 1971). What they fail to do, however, is to define the "real self."

The real self, which I prefer to call the true self, is indeed, much harder to define. In *The Thirst for Wholeness: Attachment, Addiction, and the Spiritual Path*, Christina Grof (1993) calls it the Deeper Self, which is connected with a divine force. John Firman and Ann Gila, in *The Primal Wound: A Transpersonal View of Trauma, Addiction and Growth* (1997), speak of the true self and the Transpersonal Self, which is also considered to be a part of a greater force. Karen Walant speaks of the Alienated Self in her book, *Creating the Capacity for Attachment: Treating Addictions and the Alienated Self* (1995). It is difficult, in fact, to find a definition for the true self that does not include some sort of spiritual aspect.

Spirituality is important to many people, and it can be a useful tool in recovery. It is possible, however, to view the true self and to recover from addiction without spirituality. I have developed what I feel is a rational, cognitive definition of true self.

The true self is the basis of our personality before we are influenced by the beliefs, both rational and irrational, that help make up the social self; it should be a major part of our self-concept. The true self is inherent in all people; there are aspects of it that do not rely on nature or nurture.

I would, then, state that there are four aspects of self: the physical self, the social self, the self-concept, and the true self. The process of recovery involves restoring connection to the true self and rebuilding the self-concept in a manner that more accurately reflects the true self.

A common theme in the literature on addiction and self is the addict's sense of emptiness or being alone. Craig Nakken, in *The Addictive Personality: Understanding Compulsion in Our Lives* (1988) states that, "no matter what the addiction is, every addict engages in a relationship with an object or event in order to produce a desired mood change." The mood change is needed to fill a sense of emptiness. While there are many ways of defining that sense of emptiness, I see it as the need for the true self.

There has also been a tendency in addiction treatment to undervalue the need for self-awareness and self-sufficiency. The general belief is that the self is what led to the addiction, and something beside the self is needed to overcome the addiction. The addict is seen as being self-centered, which contributes to the addiction. It is my view that disconnection from the true self is what keeps the addiction active and that true self-awareness will aid recovery. Nakken (1998) makes a very compelling argument for this view in the following statement:

> "Some people say that addicts are self-centered. I strongly disagree. Instead, addicts are Addict-centered at a cost to the Self. The process of recovery from the illness of addiction is found in Self-renewal. For us to recover, there has to be a rededication or dedication to Self. In other words, the Self must become important again" (Nakken, 1998).

The "Self" that Nakken refers to is what I call the true self, which needs to become a major influence on the self-concept.

There is a strong belief that there is a genetic predisposition to alcohol and drug addiction. It is also obvious that the physical effects of alcohol and other drugs affect the physical self; this, in turn, affects the self-concept. Once the presence or absence of a substance defines the physical self and the self-concept adapts to that definition, the person is separated to a degree from the true self.

As the social self develops, the person is exposed to various messages that also help to build the self-concept. Some of these messages are accurate gauges of the person and their interactions with others. There are messages, however, that reflect the self-concept of others;

these messages may not accurately apply to the developing person. If that person should incorporate them into the developing self-concept, the result is a disconnection between the true self and the self-concept.

While the self-concept begins its formation early in life, it is not static. The self-concept continues to change and grow as a person experiences life. This self-concept may play a role in the person's addiction; at the same time, the addiction also plays a role in the self-concept.

If a person grows up in an addicted family, the self-concept of that person can be built on inaccurate messages. Some may feel as though they are the cause of problems in the family. Others may believe that life is unpredictable and that there is no prevailing sense of order. Some may come to believe that mood-altering substances are a necessary coping strategy for life. There are countless irrational messages that can be incorporated into the self-concept when a person grows up in an addicted household. A person can incorporate similar messages even if they do not grow up in an addicted environment, but the chances of these influences are increased by their presence in an addicted family.

Once a person begins the process of addiction the outside influences on the self-concept become powerful enough to cause a further disconnection from the true self. As the need for the substance becomes more powerful, the physical self more heavily influences the self-concept. As a person becomes more physically dependent on a substance, interactions with others begin to change. This affects the self-concept.

In addiction, a person may begin to distrust feedback from other people as these people are expressing concern about the extent of the effects of the substance on the person and their relationships. At the same time, guilt and shame may also influence the self-concept. The addicted person may have difficulty accepting that their behavior is a result of the substance and may begin to view him or herself as "bad." As a result, their self-concept becomes based on the idea that they are in some way flawed.

As addiction progresses, the person may become involved in behaviors that are far removed from the true self. They are caught within a self-concept that is shaped and defined by drug use. They must use the drug in order to meet the expectations of that addicted self-concept.

As we consider recovery from addiction, it is important to realize that abstinence from alcohol and drug use is only the start of a long and difficult process. Recovery from addiction must include recovery of the true self and incorporation of the true self into the self-concept. This is neither as easy nor as difficult as it may sound. There are a number of things that can be done to help restore connection with the true self; these things take time, effort, and patience, but they are effective.

It is important to identify what comprises the true self. This is a process of self-examination. I have found several questions are helpful in this process. First, a person needs to examine beliefs.

What do I believe about myself? What do I believe about others? What do I believe about the world around me?

Once these beliefs are known, it may be necessary to examine them to determine if they are rational or irrational. Irrational beliefs lead to a disconnection from the true self. These can be disputed using the REBT techniques outlined in the next chapter. Rational beliefs can be used to strengthen the connection with the true self.

Other questions also can be used to redefine and rebuild the true self. What is important to me? What moral or ethical guidelines do I feel that I must follow? What must I have to feel fulfilled and at peace? What do I want from life for myself and for others? These questions require careful thought. It is important to differentiate between what the individual really wants and needs and what they have been made to feel they want and need.

Another way to reconnect with the true self is to evaluate strengths and weaknesses. During active addiction a person tends to lose track of both of these. They feel too weak to acknowledge strengths and too strong to admit to any weakness. Making a list of strengths and weaknesses gives a person a clearer view of the true self, for these are components of the true self. When a person can acknowledge both strengths and weaknesses, they also achieve a balanced sense of self.

Meditation is also an effective method of connecting with the true self. This is not necessarily a "spiritual" practice; meditation is quieting the mind, getting beyond the social self, to hear the voice of the true self. There is no special way to meditate to connect with the true self, no mantras or special positions. A person simply needs to find a quiet space, a comfortable position, and to allow everyday thoughts and concerns to be forgotten. In the quiet, a person's "inner voice" becomes clearer. During this process a person may become more aware of inner messages; these can then be evaluated to determine if they are affirming or destructive messages.

Guided visualization can also be effective in connecting with the true self. While it is similar to meditation, it is also a form of self-hypnosis. Again, the focus is on relaxation and clearing the mind of everyday thoughts and concerns. In guided visualizations, however, spoken suggestions are given to help guide the person's thinking in a way to promote self-awareness. In a visualization to connect with the true self, the suggestions would probably include walking a path, going deeper into a place such as a forest. The person would be instructed to continue relaxing as they travel the path. The person might be instructed to take note of any obstacles found on the path, but to move past the obstacles. The person would be led to a clearing where they will take time to notice the surroundings, thoughts, and feelings. The person would then be brought back along the path to their starting point. These visualizations can be relaxing and informative. Recorded guided visualizations are available, or a person may record his or her own visualization.

There is a sample visualization in the appendix of this book.

These approaches to restoring connection with the true self are, at first, uncomfortable for people in recovery. I have had many clients voice reluctance at spending time reflecting on the questions of beliefs, values and needs. Often, they will give quick, short, and superficial answers to those questions. I have had people tell me later that the questions prompted them to really reflect and that they have been surprised at what they discovered. Many of them also note that their actions have been extremely far removed from their beliefs and values. This leads them to begin building a new self-concept that is more closely aligned to the true self.

In the Twelve-Step approach, there is an emphasis on finding a "Higher Power," which is generally considered to be a supernatural power known as God. This works for many people but does not work for everyone. For those who have trouble with the concept of God, I feel that this higher power can be the true self. When a person in recovery finds the true self, they have found a power that is greater than the self-concept that was created through, and kept alive through, their addiction. If the person does indeed have a spiritual basis the need for self-awareness and connection is still an important part of the recovery process.

Chapter Eight:
Cognitive/Behavioral Techniques

This chapter will examine the history of Rational Emotive Behavior Therapy (REBT) as developed by Albert Ellis. It will also explore how Ellis has applied it to addiction treatment and how Jack Trimpey, founder of Rational Recovery, expanded this application. I will briefly comment on the struggle between Rational Recovery and Alcoholics Anonymous. Finally, I will discuss how these techniques are useful for treating people for alcoholism.

Albert Ellis, founder of REBT, was trained in psychoanalysis. Over time, Ellis began to doubt the effectiveness of psychoanalysis, with its emphasis on uncovering past traumas. Ellis came to believe that discovering the faulty beliefs that led to irrational behaviors could treat the problems that his patients presented. In 1955, Ellis first developed Rational Emotive Therapy (RET). Ellis changed this to Rational Emotive Behavior Therapy (REBT) around 1995. For the sake of clarity, and to acknowledge Ellis' continued work, I will refer to it as REBT. This approach was first presented in the 1957 book, *How to Live with a Neurotic*. The definitive book on the subject was *A Guide to Rational Living*, written by Ellis and Robert Harper, first published in 1961.

Ellis believes that the basis of most emotional disturbance is the presence of irrational beliefs. His philosophy is often briefly stated as "you feel what you feel because you think what you think." In other words, people do not respond to specific events; they react to what they *believe* about the event. If the person has an irrational belief, the event will trigger an irrational response. REBT offers the following formula to demonstrate the process:

A $\leftrightarrow$ B $\leftrightarrow$ C
(activating event)   (belief)   (emotional / behavioral consequence)

To help clarify this approach, I will present a "real life" example of this theory. John is currently in treatment for cocaine dependence. His wife, Mary, tells him, "I have been hurt by your actions while you were using." John pulls away from his wife and begins to curse and throw things. John is not reacting to what Mary said. If he were, he would not have such an extreme reaction. John is reacting to irrational beliefs that he holds. Perhaps he believes that he is unlovable unless he is perfect. It may be that he believes that any negative feedback is total rejection. Whatever the belief may be, the consequence is in reaction to the belief, not the event.

REBT offers a way to deal with these messages. First, a person needs to identify the irrational messages that affect them. To do this, the person would review situations that resulted in irrational responses to events. They would then try to determine the belief that led to the response. After the beliefs are identified, they would use a disputing intervention to arrive at a rational effect and a new feeling. Here is an expansion of the earlier diagram, showing the REBT process:

104

A	←→	B	←→	C
(activating event)		(belief)		(emotional and behavioral
consequence)				

↓

D	←→	E	←→	F
(disputing intervention)		(new effect)		(new feeling)

In this diagram, "D" is the disputing intervention; a three-step process designed to challenge the irrational beliefs. After first detecting the irrational belief, the person debates these beliefs by learning how to logically question them and effectively stop believing them. The third step is to discriminate rational beliefs from irrational beliefs. This disputing technique leads to "E," an effective, rational philosophy. This philosophy helps create "F," a new set of feelings.

To return to the earlier example, John would examine his irrational response to Mary's statement. He may discover that he has the irrational belief that any negative feedback is total rejection. He disputes this by telling himself that no one is perfect, and Mary has the right to feel as she does. He tells himself that he is still acceptable even though he may have faults. As a result, he is better able to respond to Mary and others who give him constructive criticism. This leads to a new feeling that is based on rational thought.

REBT suggests that pronounced feelings of failure, beliefs in worthlessness, unthinking acceptances of other's condemnation, and self-damning tendencies are not justified, "not because they emerge as absolutely wrong or wicked, or because they contradict the laws of God or the universe. But simply because, on good pragmatic grounds, they almost always prove self-defeating and needlessly prevent us from getting many of the things that we desire" (Ellis & Harper, 1975).

There are five core irrational beliefs that people are likely to hold. The first one is identified by Ellis as "Musturbation," also known as shoulding or demandingness. An example of this is the belief, "I have to (should, must, ought to, deserve to) do well and be approved by people I like or else I am an inadequate, worthless person!" Almost any beliefs with words like must, should, ought, or deserve are likely to be irrational. Awfulizing beliefs are identified in this sentence, "It's awful, terrible, horrible, catastrophic when I don't perform well (as I must), when you don't give me what I need (as you should), and when conditions frustrate me (as they must not)!" Low Frustration Tolerance is identified in statements such as, "I can't stand (bear, tolerate) it when I don't get what I need (as I must) or when I do get what I don't want (and must not get)." Rating and blaming beliefs can be, "I am a worthless and damnable person for behaving poorly (as I must not behave)!" Finally, overgeneralizing, an always or never attitude, can be seen in the belief, "When I do poorly (as I must not) or things are bad (as they must not be), that proves I'll never be happy, succeed, or get what I want" (Ellis & Velton, 1992).

Some people may feel these statements are so extreme that no one could possibly hold them as beliefs. In my experience, they are really quite common, especially among people with substance addiction problems. The use of REBT techniques to dispute these messages can provide a person with a way to eliminate the message as well as the consequence of the belief.

Ellis presents REBT as an effective tool for treating chemical dependency. He co-authored two books that explore the use of REBT for addictions. *When AA Doesn't Work for You: Rational Steps for Quitting Alcohol*, written with Emmett Velton, is written for the layperson, while *Rational Emotive Therapy with Alcoholics and Substance Abusers*, written with John McInerney, Raymond DiGiuseppe, and Raymond Yeager is a professional's guide. In *When AA Doesn't Work for You: Rational Steps for Quitting Alcohol*, the authors present REBT's three insights. These are:

Insight One: Your current feelings and actions have causes. The most important causes of your addictions are your thoughts, attitudes, images, memories, and other cognitions. This is what REBT calls B, your belief system, especially your stinking thinking or irrational beliefs.

Insight Two: Wherever your belief systems originated (parents, family, society, traumas, biology, self-inventions), you carry them on now and actively believe and follow them. You steadily reindoctrinate yourself in them today and sometimes actively fight off other's attempts to get you to change them.

Insight Three: You require hard, persistent work to change your beliefs, actions, and feelings, to practice new ones, and to avoid returning to old ones. Further, your human condition tends to give new problems and stresses. So insight is not the main watchword. Eternal vigilance plus much work and practice is (Ellis & Velton, 1992).

This approach stands somewhat in opposition to a strict disease model of addiction but is not totally inconsistent with the disease model presented in the first chapter. It acknowledges that biology may play a role in addiction as it could affect irrational beliefs. It also acknowledges the role that cognition plays in recovery. This approach differs from AA as it suggests that people have the power to change their beliefs; this is in contrast to the AA statement that a person is powerless over their addiction.

In *Rational Emotive Therapy with Alcoholics and Substance Abusers*, Ellis offers more specific information on ways that beliefs can affect recovery and ways to deal with those beliefs. One attitude or belief that is common is that abstinence from mood-altering substances is a curse. A person with that belief will find that recovery is a burden and is likely to return to using. That person can use the techniques of REBT to change the belief to one of recovery as an opportunity to improve the quality of life.

Another attitudinal barrier is self-pity. If a person feels sorry for himself or herself because other people can use substances "responsibly" while they cannot, they may decide to go back to substance use no matter the consequence. People with this attitude need to tell themselves that other people are able to do a lot of things that they cannot do; what matters is what they *can* do, which includes living a clean and sober life.

Some people will think, "Drinking and drugging is not a problem for me; it is other people who have a problem with the way I drink and use." The rational belief for disputing that is, "If my drinking or using is a problem for others, it soon will be for me if it is not already a problem."

Another common attitude is that sobriety will be too hard, and the person might lose friends, be bored or uncomfortable. To combat that attitude, people should tell themselves that, while it may take some time and effort, they may lose much more if they continue to use.

Feeling as though they cannot stand to not have another drink or drug is another common attitude for people in recovery. They need to admit that abstinence is difficult, but they have endured other difficulties in the past. They should also remember that, while they may *want* to have another drink or drug, they do not *need* to have it (Ellis, et. al., 1988).

Another contribution to cognitive treatment of addiction is the work of Jack Trimpey, founder of Rational Recovery. Mr. Trimpey is a person who has dealt with his own alcohol problem; like many, he first went to AA to try to find help. Trimpey found the religious aspects of AA, and the "our way or the highway" attitude of many within the group, to be too uncomfortable. As a result, he decided to develop another approach to treating addiction. As a practicing social worker, Trimpey was familiar with Ellis and the REBT process. Trimpey used this as a basis for his Rational Recovery program.

Trimpey has added important techniques to cognitive/behavioral addiction treatment of addiction. These techniques, however, are protected by proprietary trademark, so I will not elaborate on them. He presents his views in two books, *The Small Book*, and *Rational Recovery: The New Cure for Substance Addiction*. These techniques are extremely useful and, on the surface, appear to be acceptable to anyone in recovery. Yet, there is great enmity and argument between Rational Recovery (RR) and Alcoholics Anonymous (AA). I feel that the reasons for this need to be examined.

Prior to the founding of AA, treatment of alcoholism was not highly effective. AA appeared to work for many people. As AA became widely publicized, people in the treatment community began to see AA as "the answer"- the only way that people could recover from alcohol addiction. These same principles were then applied to drug users through Narcotics Anonymous.

The problem with viewing any form of addiction treatment as the only form of treatment is that it does not take into account the diversity of human beings. Just as some people are helped by a medication that causes an allergic reaction in others, not all people will respond to a specific mode of treatment. AA may work well for some; for others the approach may cause extreme adverse reactions.

110

The creation of RR would seem to solve a problem, offering people in treatment, and treatment providers, a choice of treatment approaches. Unfortunately, this is not what happened. Part of the problem undoubtedly lies in the fact that there are those who staunchly present AA as the only effective treatment approach for addiction, and who accuse anyone presenting a differing view of practicing bad medicine and jeopardizing the lives of people with addiction problems.

Another part of the problem is the manner in which Trimpey presented his Rational Recovery approach. For example, the "bible" of AA is the book, *Alcoholics Anonymous*, which is commonly known as "the Big Book." The title of Trimpey's first book, *The Small Book*, was an obvious poke at AA. The book seems to spend as much time talking about what is wrong with AA as it does presenting RR. Three of the thirteen chapters of the book contain the words "take sides." It is not surprising that RR offended people in AA.

I believe that there is a need for multiple treatment approaches to treat the diverse population of people with addiction. Rather than present any program as "the" program, we need to have a variety of options to choose from. In addition, treatment providers and clients should feel free to blend treatment approaches in order to best meet the needs of each individual. As Dianne Doyle Pita states in her book, *Addictions Counseling*, "There are enough addicted people to go around. No one needs to corner the market" (Pita, 1998).

Cognitive/Behavioral Therapy is considered an evidence-based treatment approach; it has become an integral part of many treatment programs. It works especially well in the MAR treatment plan as well as in drug-free treatment.

Irrational messages play a major role in the development and continuation of addictive disease. MAR counselors need to stress the need to become aware of these irrational messages and encourages the use of REBT to dispute those messages.

I use these techniques with the clients I see. It is not at all unusual to have a client tell me that "I wanted to use," or "I needed the drug." I have them look at the statement and to learn to change the "I wanted/needed" to "It wanted/needed." I have had several clients report that this technique alone has increased their ability to resist drug use. Several other clients have reported discovering irrational beliefs that have led them to drug use. Most clients need to be reminded that overcoming irrational beliefs is a process; many expect the messages to disappear once they have been identified and wonder what they have done wrong because the belief returns.

REBT is a great, short-term approach for treating addiction and is, therefore, especially good for those in medication assisted recovery programs. The person's engagement with us may have a limited period of time, especially if insurance companies are involved. REBT allows us to teach skills in a short period of time that the person can practice over the course of their lives. It is not a replacement for long-term recovery support, but it does have a life beyond the counseling relationship. The use of REBT is as consistent with twelve-step based treatment and can only improve the effectiveness of addiction treatment.

Chapter Nine:
Communication Skills for Recovery

Surprisingly, I have found truly little is said about the importance of communication in the process of recovery. A literature search using the key words "addiction" and "communication" did not offer a single match. I find this interesting, as I believe communication plays a vital role in the recovery process.

In my mind, communication is a vital part of many of the recovery process. In order to take responsibility for past actions a person must be able to express their regret in a manner that allows the person to whom it is addressed to comprehend and respond appropriately. Communication is also important in identifying and expressing feelings. Communication is also needed to restore connection with significant people and to make connection with others who will support recovery.

Communication also is needed to let the addiction professionals know the level of the client's compliance with treatment and the areas that they need to work on. If the person cannot communicate these needs, the doctors and counselors cannot be fully effective.

This idea is fully supported by the work of Carl Rogers. He states that a "neurotic" person is in trouble first because he or she cannot communicate within his or her self; and, as long as this is true, there are distortions in the way the person communicates with others. He further states that the task of counseling is to first improve the inner communication and then to improve communication with others (Rogers, 1961). In my view, the inner communication is learned as a person restores the true self. The next task is to improve communication with others.

In the following pages I will present some basics of communication theory that help to set a foundation for rules of communication. I will briefly discuss the effect of rational and irrational beliefs on communication. Finally, I will present several communication skills that will aid the recovery process.

At the heart of communication theory is the concept of the sender and the receiver. Take, for example, a radio station and your car radio. The station sends out the message, but there is no guarantee that you will receive that message. If you are not in the car, you will not receive it. If the radio is off, you will not receive it. If you are tuned to a different station, you will not receive it. If you drive out of range of the station, you will not receive it. The same holds true for interpersonal communication.

There are many things that can prevent a message from being received in interpersonal communication. I will look at these in more detail later, but some common problems are differences of interpretation, irrational beliefs, and inattentive listening.

In *Bridges Not Walls: A Book about Interpersonal Communication*, John Stewart presents five basic facts about communication. They are:

1. No one person can completely control a communication event, and no single person or action causes – or can be blamed for – a communication outcome.

2. Culture figures prominently in the communication process. Ethnicity, gender, age, social class, sexual orientation, and other cultural features always affect communication and are affected by it.

3. Some of the most important meanings people collaboratively construct are identities; all communication involves negotiating identities or selves.

4. The most influential communication events are conversations.

5. The most useful single communication skill is "nexting," which is asking yourself, "What can I help to happen next, or how?" (Stewart, 1999)

Each of these facts holds an important message about communication. The first one makes the point that communication is something that involves two or more people; each plays a role in the process. As a result, all parties have responsibility for the successful, or unsuccessful, outcome of the communication event. This requires that all parties make an effort to keep the process moving efficiently.

I feel that the most important point made by Stewart in the above is the second, that of the effect of culture on communication. I remember one of my adolescent clients who commented on the Birkenstock shoes I was wearing. The comment was, "Those are really fat shoes." I began to respond that, while the toe was wider than normal, they were not really fat. The client laughed at this point, and explained that they were "phat," meaning, to my generation, cool. This is an example of the effect of culture on communication.

This applies as well to differences in socialization. While men and women may not be from different planets, their social training is usually different. Women may be raised to value specific traits, such as openness and vulnerability; men are often taught that these traits are signs of weakness. Racial, economic, and social differences can also result in differing values and understandings. When communication seems blocked, it may be the result of such differences.

The third fact simply points out that identity issues are always involved in communication. A person's self-image has an affect on the way they listen and respond in a communication event. This can especially come into play where irrational messages affect a person's self-image.

The fourth fact points out that conversation, our most ordinary form of communication, is also the most important. This is one reason for learning communication skills. The fifth fact points out that the most important communication skill is to keep the communication flowing.

Communication is an important part of any relationship. Effective communication requires listening skills as well as speaking skills. Before we can listen to others, however, we must be able to listen to ourselves. Many people feel that self-awareness is a selfish thing. In reality, it is vital to any type of interaction in life. Our relationship to other people, to nature, and to society is affected by our ability to know and to accept ourselves.

I explored the effects of subconscious, irrational messages in the examination of the use of cognitive/behavioral techniques in MAR. These messages can be a major hindrance to any type of communication. That chapter demonstrated how these messages affect listening; a person might hear and react to echoes from the past rather than the voice of the present. Recognizing these messages and their effects are part of the communication process.

As a person is able to recognize these messages and the effect that they have, he or she will be increasingly able to communicate from a space beyond the effect of those messages. In some cases, it may be possible to tell a person that the response is a reaction to "flashes from the past." In other cases, a person may need to be able to move his or her self to a space beyond those messages, or to adjust their reaction in a way that negates the power of the message. Again, the REBT process is an excellent way to deal with these situations.

If a person has learned to be afraid of their feelings, they may find it difficult to admit their feelings to themselves and to other people. This inability to face feelings can be a major hindrance for communication in relationships. If for instance, a person is afraid of being rejected, he or she may find it difficult to express his or her needs to another person. In order to avoid having to share needs and face rejection, they may suppress the need, trying to pretend that it isn't there. This denial does not eliminate that need; it will surface somehow. An unexpressed and unacknowledged need, however, often reveals itself in a less than desirable fashion. It is far better to learn to express one's feelings and needs than to repress them. An unexpressed need that reveals itself through inappropriate behavior causes problems that must then be discussed; the behavior adds to the problem.

People in recovery should also be aware that other people may have buried messages and that they may or may not be aware of them. If communication is a problem, they should look at interactions in the relationship to see if the other person is also reacting to something other than the current conversation. If so, let the nature of the relationship decide the reaction to the situation. In an intimate relationship, they may want to point out that the person seems to be reacting to something other than the present situation. In less intimate relationships, it may be necessary to make allowances for the person's actions.

There are techniques and skills that can be used to improve communication, some of which will be presented here. When people first start using them, they often report feeling uncomfortable. Clients should be encouraged to continue the use of these techniques, as they will become more automatic, and more comfortable, with practice.

One of the better-known techniques is the use of "I" statements; also called "I" messages. This is a way to express one's interests directly without evoking unnecessary defensiveness in the other person (Guilar, 2001). As an example, a person might feel frustrated that a significant other is not demonstrating a proper amount of trust. If that person says, "You hurt me when you don't trust me," then the significant other is likely to respond in a defensive manner. If, on the other hand, the person states, "I feel hurt that you don't trust me," then the door is left open for discussion rather than debate. This is simply a matter of accepting responsibility for one's own feelings and beliefs.

There are four components of an effective "I" message. First, as already stated, is ownership of the feeling or belief. The second is a statement of the problem. The third component is a statement of the intermediate goal; what the person would like to have happen. The final component is to express the reason for wanting this goal to be met (Guilar, 2001).

There are some things to keep in mind in using this tool. First, a proper "I" statement takes responsibility for feelings and beliefs. The statement, "I want you to stop hurting me," is not an effective "I" message, as it opens the door for argument as to whether or the person is actually being hurtful. On the other hand, stating, "I feel hurt by what you say, and I really don't like feeling that," would allow the person to then discuss what is hurtful and why the person perceives it in that manner.

I heard of a supervisor, who would say to her employees, "I'm going to give you an 'I' message." That statement negated any positive effect that the "I" message may have had. In making that announcement, the supervisor was implying that the person she was addressing was at fault. The supervisor also implied that she was going to be generous by giving that feedback in a nice manner, even though the other was in the wrong. That defeats the purpose of the technique.

Another effective technique is to confirm the other person's point of view. This does not mean that you have to agree with it; it is simply trying to see the situation as the other person sees it (Guilar, 2001). I have already discussed how attitudes and beliefs can affect communication. This is the process of trying to understand the point of view of the receiver. While this may not resolve the problem, it gives one a better chance of finding a solution. Knowing the backdrop of the other person's viewpoint can help in confirming that person's view. It is important to talk from your own point of view. Avoid saying things like, "You just think that..." or "You just wanted to..." as these statements assume knowledge of the other person's feelings and motives. Also, avoid saying things like, "I know how you feel." You may empathize with the person, but you cannot possibly know how they feel.

There are other ways to improve communication. One is to stay as positive as the situation permits. Avoid name-calling, sarcasm, threats, and intimidation. If you are talking about a behavior you don't like, attack the behavior, not the person. When possible, try to offer suggestions for solutions to a problem. Use the "sandwich" method when presenting information that could be perceived as negative; say something positive, offer the correction, then follow it with a positive statement. For example, you might say, "You have been very supportive of my recovery. I wish you could be more patient with my progress. I know you are doing your best to be understanding."

Another way to improve communication is by being clear and specific. Make your point clearly; ask for what you want and tell how you feel. Avoid saying that a person "always" or "never" does something. If you are going to quote what someone said, be accurate; if you are talking about someone's actions, give specific times and examples. Avoid exaggeration and stick to what is relevant.

It is also important to keep communication a two-way process. Do not monopolize; allow the other person a chance to respond while they can remember what is on their mind. Ask for feedback, for example, "Please tell me what you understood me to say." If the person did not understand, it allows you to rephrase the statement in a way that insures understanding.

Another aid to good communication is to stay on the subject. If possible, organize your thoughts ahead of time. Discuss one topic at a time and don't bring up issues that are already settled. Also, avoid "kitchen sinking," bringing up every problem and issue at one time.

Finally, good listening is an important part of communication. It is common to say, "I hear you." There is a big difference, however, between hearing and listening. Hearing is a physiological process of decoding sounds. Listening, on the other hand, is a process that involves four activities – selecting, attending, understanding, and remembering. These will lead to responding (Beebe, Beebe, and Redmond, 1999).

Selecting is the process of focusing on one sound out of the various sounds competing for attention. Sound is all around us; we are frequently unaware of many of the sounds. Yet, for effective communication, a person must choose to attend to the voice of the person that is speaking and try to filter out other sounds. Attending is focusing in on that sound. Attention can be fleeting, and people tend to focus on sounds that meet their needs or are consistent with what they think they should focus on. Attending is easier when a person feels they will be invited to participate or respond to what is being said.

Understanding is the process of assigning meaning to the sounds that are selected and attended to. I have already discussed ways that differences in culture and language can affect understanding. It is important for a person to assure that he or she understands the message that was given. One way to do this is for the listener to paraphrase what he understood the speaker to say, and to ask the speaker to confirm that the interpretation is correct. If it is not, then the speaker has the opportunity to clarify what was said. The final activity in listening is remembering. A person must remember what was said so that they may respond to it (Beebe, Beebe, and Redmond, 1999).

There are various modes of listening. There is active, or participatory, listening. This is an expressive form of listening. A person lets the speaker know they are listening through a variety of verbal and non-verbal cues. These include maintaining eye contact, focusing directly on the speaker, using facial expressions to show feelings and reactions, asking appropriate questions, and signaling understanding through phrases like "I see." To aid this process, a person should focus on the speaker, which is the process of selection that was discussed earlier. A person should also avoid the mistake of tuning out the speaker while planning his or her own next statement or allowing the thoughts to stray to unrelated topics. A person should also assume that there is value in what the speaker has to say. This makes the listening process easier (DeVito, 1998).

It is important at times to understand what a person feels in order to understand what they mean; this is empathic listening. In order to do this, a person should view the speaker as an equal; try to understand both the thoughts and feelings, and to avoid prejudging what the speaker has to say. The listener tries to imagine his or her self in the place of the speaker.

I agree with Carl Rogers that communication is important, and that, in general, effective communication is not commonplace. Rogers states, "To understand another person's thoughts and feelings thoroughly, with the meanings they have for him, and to be thoroughly understood by this other person in return – this is one of the most rewarding of human experiences, and all too rare" (Rogers, 1961). Effective recovery is really nothing more than effective living, and good communication is one of the keys to achieve that.

Chapter Ten:
A Positive Approach to Relapse Prevention

The subject of relapse prevention and treatment is a major focus in the field of addiction counseling. Most insurance authorization forms ask if the client has developed a relapse prevention plan. Some treatment centers offer a special program for people who have relapsed after a period of sobriety. Terence Gorski, a well-known leader in the addiction field, has specialized in relapse prevention and treatment. His CENAPS® Corporation offers classes and special certification for Relapse Specialists.

While I recognize that relapse is a possibility in the recovery process, I also feel that the constant focus on relapse is not of benefit to clients. I find that a focus on "not failing" may actually set people up to fail in their recovery. I prefer to have clients focus on building and maintaining recovery; in doing this, they ultimately end up preventing relapse.

In this chapter I define relapse and explore several theories of relapse. I also explore how Gorski and Ellis view relapse and evaluate the strengths and weaknesses of those views. I then offer a new way to address relapse prevention and treatment. I will also discuss the need to convince clients that they need a solid plan once the medication is stopped.

In general, relapse is a return to use of alcohol and other drugs. Gorski defines it in this way:

"Relapse is a process that occurs within the patient and manifests itself in a progressive pattern of behavior that reactivates the symptoms of a disease or creates related debilitating conditions in a person that has previously experienced remission from the illness" (Gorski & Miller, 1982).

Perhaps the most important element of this definition is the idea of relapse as a process. Gorski suggests that the actual use of the drug is the end of the process. Gorski also emphasizes that the process occurs within the patient. While it is typical for a person to blame the relapse on outside forces, Gorski states that relapse patterns are formed by "attitudes, values, and behavioral responses that occur inside the patient" (Gorski & Miller, 1982).

How much of a problem is relapse in addiction treatment? Gorski states that "many, if not most, return to the use of alcohol at least once after making an honest commitment to sobriety and pursuing a structured recovery program" (Gorski & Miller, 1982). I have seen many clients return for inpatient and outpatient treatment several times within a three-year period.

Gorski suggests that relapse prevention must begin in the early phases of recovery. According to Gorski, "Relapse is not a conscious choice, but the end result of a conscious, but progressive, sequence of warning signs (Gorski & Miller, 1982)." If a person is able to identify these signs, they can stop the relapse before it leads to the use of the substance.

Gorski has compiled a list of thirty-seven warning signs. I will not list all the warning signs but will look at a few of the more common ones as well as a few that seem harder to comprehend.

One sign is a return to the denial that first prevented a person from getting into treatment. The person begins to question the need for total abstinence and may decide that he or she is capable of controlling drug use. Another warning sign, according to Gorski, is an adamant commitment to sobriety. While this sounds as though it would be positive, Gorski states that a person can become so convinced that they will never use drugs again, that he or she stops pursuing a recovery program, thus becoming prone to relapse.

Another sign is tendencies toward loneliness. The person increases isolation and avoidance of interactions with others. Loss of constructive planning is another relapse warning sign. Gorski states wishful thinking begins to replace planning and effort.

Gorski differentiates between therapeutic and non-therapeutic relapses. A therapeutic relapse is defined as a relapse that increases the chances of full recovery because it points out the "undeniable fact" that the person is addicted and cannot drink or use drugs. This is usually a short-term problem with low consequences. A non-therapeutic relapse is one that makes recovery more difficult. This is usually of a long-term nature, but even a short-term relapse can be non-therapeutic if it results in more extreme consequences.

Gorski suggests the use of relapse prevention support groups as a tool in avoiding and recovering from relapse. In his book, *How to Start a Relapse Prevention Support Group,* Gorski outlines a suggested structure for these groups, the membership requirements, how the relapse prevention group differs from an AA meeting, the need for sponsors, as well as answering the question, "When is relapse prevention finished?" His answer to that question is that the problem never goes away. As he states in that section, "We suffer from a disease called alcoholism, not 'alcohol*was*m'" (Gorski, 1989).

Albert Ellis, in *When AA Doesn't Work for You: Rational Steps to Quitting Alcohol*, offers a different view of relapse. While he agrees with AA that recovery is a life-long process, he does not view addiction as a disease that is chronic and life-long. He states, "you can recover from substance abuse – after all, millions of people have done so. *But you can never recover from being human"* (Ellis & Velton, 1992).

Being human, Ellis states, is being fallible. He states that the beliefs that support addiction are not part of a disease; they are simply human nature. It is the escalation of wants and desires into demands and musts. He also points out that being human means having the ability to change and transform one's self. He warns that people often think being "normal," as in "not addicted," will mean ecstasy, or at least a better feeling than one had while addicted. Ellis states that a person must be ready to accept that life without the drug will consist of ups and downs that are, after all, normal. The key to preventing relapse, according to Ellis, is recognize the irrational messages that support continued drug use and to dispute them using the Rational-Emotive Behavior Therapy (REBT) techniques.

Ellis agrees with Gorski that drinking or drug use does not lead to relapse. He, like Gorski, states that the use of the drug is the end of the process. He also suggests signs of relapse; most of them regarding irrational thought and messages, often referred to as "stinking thinking" in the recovery field. If a person can recognize the resurgence of these irrational messages, they can stop the process before it leads to drug use.

Each approach has strengths and weaknesses. While Gorski's model of relapse as a process is helpful, I find that the emphasis on relapse in addiction treatment is, in my experience, often counter-productive. I would sometimes have a client enter my outpatient group after completing an inpatient stay. They might remain clean for several weeks, but then would test positive for drugs or alcohol. When the results were presented to them, the usual reply was, "They said in inpatient that addiction is a disease of relapse." This served as a justification to the client; they were simply following the course of the disease. I also feel that long-term attendance in a relapse prevention support group is counterproductive. It keeps the person's focus on fear of failure.

Not surprisingly, I find the most affinity with Albert Ellis' approach to relapse. I am a firm believer in the effect of attitudes and beliefs on feelings and behaviors. I also agree with Ellis, as well as with Gorski, that relapse is a process, and that one can learn to recognize the warning signs and to make changes to prevent relapse before it happens. I do, however, feel that there are more causes of relapse than attitudes and beliefs and feel that these also need to be examined.

After looking at these two approaches to relapse prevention, I have come to find a view of relapse prevention that is compatible with both 12-Step programs and medication assisted recovery. Both the Gorski and the Ellis approaches have an influence, but my approach is more than a sum of its parts.

To begin, I do not talk about relapse prevention. Gorski states, "Recovery and relapse are two sides of the same coin" (Gorski & Miller, 1982). I agree completely with this statement. That is why, in my approach, the emphasis is on building and maintaining recovery rather than preventing relapse. It is, after all, the same thing. Maintaining recovery, however, presents a positive goal as opposed to the negative goal of preventing relapse. If one concentrates on the possibility of failure, failure is always hovering nearby. On the other hand, focusing on a successful recovery helps to build and strengthen that recovery. I presented this view to a group of clients recently; one asked me to repeat it and requested that I write it for him. All were excited about focusing on building recovery as opposed to preventing relapse.

I had a client in group who stated that he "always" relapsed after 90 days of "clean time." He would come to group each time stating, "It's

79 days," then, "It's 85 days." Each time, you could hear the apprehension in his voice become more pronounced. He was so focused on relapse that he was not able to allow himself to focus on recovery. He was a prime candidate for the building and maintaining recovery approach.

I advise clients to identify barriers to recovery and plan to overcome them. This recognizes that there are recovery barriers, but offers the assurance that one can overcome those barriers. A lapse or slip *may* happen, but it is not an inevitable event. If a person does slip, he or she is encouraged to get right back on track and to evaluate the events leading to the slip to learn how to prevent further slips. The person is also encouraged to forgive him or herself for the slip rather than building up guilt and shame.

Anyone who has been in a drug treatment program will tell you, usually in a very mechanical manner, that to prevent relapse one should change "people, places, and things." They usually can't tell you how to go about doing so, or what to do about those people, places, and things that cannot be changed. This model suggests ways to deal with these issues.

Clients are to list those people in their lives who use mood-altering substances. They then list those who can be avoided or eliminated from their life. They then list those people who cannot be avoided and are asked to consider ways of adjusting their relationship with those people to best support their recovery. They also need to list people who can support their recovery, because changing people is more than dropping negative people; it is adding positive people.

There are also places that people associate with drug or alcohol use. Being in these places can cause the person to return to using because they provide cues that will stimulate the desire for the drug. Clients are asked to list places that are associated with drug or alcohol use, and to decide which can and which cannot be avoided. They then plan what they can do to maintain recovery if they must be in one of these places. Again, they also list places that will support their recovery.

Things, in relapse prevention, are objects, sounds, smells, situations, feelings, and other items that are strongly associated with drug use and can trigger the desire to use the substance. One client told me that he had to stop watching "The Sopranos" on television, because he always would get high while watching it. If he tried watching after starting his recovery program, the desire for drug use would become overwhelming. In this model, clients are asked to list the things that may trigger drug cravings and to determine ways to deal with them.

In this model, there is also recognition that attitudes and beliefs can be barriers to recovery. In this regard, it draws heavily upon the work of Albert Ellis. The previous chapter on REBT examines some attitudes and beliefs and suggests ways to deal with them. Some of these are a negative attitude toward sobriety, self-pity, placing blame on others, and a belief that recovery is too hard. Clients are asked to examine these and other attitudes and beliefs that they might have and are then encouraged to use the ABC methods of REBT to dispute these beliefs.

My focus on recovery retention as opposed to relapse prevention, and the tools that are provided in this model, offers clients the opportunity to make positive changes in their lives. It provides structure, support, hope, and fosters self-acceptance and self-esteem. It helps clients to see recovery as an ongoing process that will improve their quality of life.

Chapter Eleven:
Medications for Mental Health

About eight years ago, I read an article in the *Addiction Counselor* magazine that quite surprised me. While I knew that there were differences of opinion in the past about the use of medication for mental health issues for people in recovery, I felt that the issue had been resolved. It seems that the difference of opinion still exists; I would be remiss if I did not address this in this book as well.

There are medications that have been developed specifically to treat addiction issues. There are, however, many people who have co-occurring disorders, an addiction plus a mental health disorder. These people must be treated for both. Since there is a shortage of people truly able to provide dual-diagnosis treatment we need to be able to work as efficiently with psychiatrists as we do physicians prescribing medication for recovery.

Historically, one reason for the concern of many addiction counselors regarding psychiatric medications is the once held belief that treating a person's mental health disorder would eliminate the addiction issue. This view has been largely abandoned, but the memory of that time lingers on.

Another concern is the misdiagnosis of addiction problems as mental illnesses. A person who is using cocaine and going from the highs of the drug's effect to the low when it wears off could easily be diagnosed as being bipolar. Giving that person mood stabilizers would not resolve the issue.

Clearly this is a place where clients need a partnership between mental health and addiction professionals. If we combine our efforts, we can help clients to meet goals and improve the quality of life.

Since I moved to Massachusetts, the bulk of my work has been in mental health clinics rather than addiction clinics. In these cases, I was the "resident addiction specialist" and would work with clients who had addictive disorders as a primary diagnosis. I had the advantage of working closely with mental health counselors and prescribers for support in dealing with the mental health issues while I could offer them help and support them with clients who had substance abuse disorders as a secondary diagnosis. I found this relationship to be both quite enlightening for me and my colleagues and greatly beneficial for the clients.

Many of the newer medications that are available for treating mental disorders work at balancing brain chemistry and are not addictive. While it is true that these medications will not "cure" the client's addiction, they do help stabilize the client to allow the client to work on building recovery skills. It makes no sense to me to suggest that the use of these medications as prescribed should be discouraged. If it helps a person in their sobriety it is a good thing. Again, it is not "the" path to recovery, but it is certainly a part of that path.

There are still some frequently prescribed medications that are addictive and are not the best choice for a client with an addiction problem. If we are willing to work with prescribers and the mental health counselors, we can help them to determine the safest and most effective course of action to treat the person's mental health disorder.

It is time that we stop seeing psychiatry as an enemy and start to explore ways that we can work as a team to meet our mutual goal of helping people to improve their quality of life.

Chapter Twelve:
The Eight Common Tasks of Positive Path Recovery

A number of the techniques that I have discussed in this book are part of my Positive Path Recovery approach. I felt that it would be good to present an overview of the Eight Principle of Positive Path Recovery and some of the worksheets related to the approach here. If you want more information, I present more detail in my book, *Positive Path Recovery: A Clinician's Guide.*

Positive Path Recovery was developed in my early years of practice. As I explored the literature and worked with clients, I began to recognize specific areas that seemed to be common to most people with addiction problems. Over a period of time, these observations developed into specific treatment goals and actions. Eventually, I distilled this into eight common recovery tasks that form the basis for Positive Path Recovery. These tasks are:

1) Admitting that the substance has taken control and committing to a path of recovery.
2) Redefining and rebuilding the sense of self. (The true self)
3) Taking responsibility and accepting forgiveness for past actions.
4) Learning to identify and express feelings.
5) Improving communication with others.

6) Restoring connection with significant people and making connection with others who can support recovery.
7) Identifying barriers to recovery and planning to overcome them.
8) Letting Go!

These are ongoing tasks rather than progressive steps. While I feel that there are certain techniques that will aid the client in these tasks, I do not impose a rigid structure on the client. I consider the client's experiences, beliefs, goals, and needs to determine the best method to treat the client.

The book, *Positive Path Recovery,* offers in-depth looks at some of the theory and techniques behind these tasks, but for now I will give a brief overview of each.

Task one uses elements of Reality Therapy to help the client recognize that the chemical use is not solving their problem and is, most likely, making things worse. It then uses the Stages of Change model and Motivational Interviewing approaches to aid in the commitment process.

For task two, there are a series of questions that are used to help the person discover the true self. This includes questions about self-image, beliefs about the world, moral and ethical guidelines, wants, needs, and goals. Guided visualization is also used to help a client look deeper within. The worksheets in the appendix offer guides for these.

Task three, taking responsibility for past actions, is another example of the use of Reality Therapy. This involves recognizing the effect that substance use had on the client and the client's friends, family, and work or school environment. Another part of this task is to accept forgiveness. This includes self-forgiveness, recognizing that excessive guilt and shame can lead to continued, or renewed, substance use.

Task four, learning to identify and express feelings, has its roots in Cognitive/Behavioral theory. Since that model suggests that feelings are based on beliefs, one must first be able to identify feelings that are affecting behavior in order to discover the beliefs behind the feelings. Ellis' REBT is a major component of this task; it is covered in more detail in Chapter Eight of this book.

Improving communication is, perhaps, not as deeply based in psychological theory as it is in basic communication theory. Some of the techniques offered to the client, however, are found in Carl Rogers' Person Centered Therapy. The need for communication skills and information on building them is covered in Chapter Nine.

Task six, restoring connection with significant people, has its roots in Family Systems Theory. One must try to restore balance to the family. Additionally, there is a need for the support of substance-free individuals. In my model, these do not have to be recovering substance abusers, although the use of AA and NA is encouraged, as there are benefits from sharing the experience of others who have faced similar problems. Additional forms of support may be other mutual support groups like SMART Recovery and Dharma Recovery, sober friends, co-workers, or others in the person's treatment program.

Task seven, identifying barriers to recovery and planning to overcome them, is, in the common terminology of addiction treatment, relapse prevention. The basics of relapse prevention, as commonly taught, are to change people, places, and things. In Positive Path Recovery, I also stress the need to change attitudes and beliefs; this is firmly rooted in the Cognitive/Behavioral model, especially in the work of Albert Ellis and Jack Trimpey. An emphasis is also made on viewing this as building recovery rather than preventing relapse. This is discussed further in Chapter Ten.

The final task of the Positive Path approach, letting go, is simply learning to move from the past. A basic tool of twelve-step treatment, the Serenity Prayer, states that a person needs to accept what they cannot change, change what they can, and to understand the difference. There is great wisdom in this. If a client tries too hard to change things that are beyond their control, the risk of frustration leading to relapse is increased. Learning to change what can be changed, such as the way a person responds to an event, can move a person along in their recovery.

The Positive Path Recovery approach is not presented as "the way" to treat addiction. It is, instead, presented as "a way" to do so. It recognizes that there are many people who have responded well to the twelve-step model of treatment. At the same time, it recognizes that there are also many who have not responded to that model and offers an alternative approach for those people.

This model can be used for anyone presenting for addiction treatment, but I feel there are some groups of people for whom this approach is especially indicated. One group would be people with one or more unsuccessful attempts at recovery through the twelve-step model. Addiction professionals often tell their clients that insanity is "doing the same thing repeatedly, expecting different results." At the same time, these professionals will offer the same treatment approach time after time. The Positive Path program offers the client a new way to approach recovery.

Another group of people who may benefit from this approach are those with strong feelings against spirituality and anything that may be perceived as "religious." There are many people who object to the "God talk" of the twelve-step model; these objections prevent them from gaining the benefit of treatment. Others may have spiritual beliefs, but find the twelve-step approach too rigidly Judeo/Christian for their comfort. It should be noted that the Positive Path is not opposed to spirituality. It does, however, recognize that spiritual belief and understanding is a very personal thing. As a result, it avoids reference to terms associated with spirituality.

People who are highly rational or self-directed may also have problems with the highly directive approach of the twelve steps. While it is true that a person in addiction probably has a history of making poor choices, it does not necessarily follow that they are incapable of making better choices. I remember hearing a co-worker once tell a client that they should not think for the first year of recovery. While I appreciate what this counselor was trying to say, I can see that it would be difficult advice to follow. The Positive Path approach teaches the person how to make healthier choices.

Positive Path Recovery is another tool that is available to the treatment professional and to the person in recovery. It should not be viewed as an attempt to undermine any present form of treatment; it is designed to expand and compliment the methods that are available in the field of substance abuse treatment.

Part Three

Client Worksheets

Chapter Thirteen:
Client Worksheets

One of the challenges of clinical work is finding royalty-free worksheets that you can use with clients. Workbooks can be costly, and counselors may not be able to afford to provide them. Many clients may not be able to afford them. I have seen some cases where people will photocopy workbooks; while the intention is good, there are ethical issues regarding the use of material that is protected by copyright that are violated in the process.

Over the years I have developed a series of client worksheets that are found in my book, How to Build and Maintain Recovery. Again, the problem is that counselors may not be able to afford to buy copies for clients. I decided that I would provide a copy of the worksheets in this volume. These worksheets may be reproduced for clinical use. You are only asked to give credit to the author for his work developing them.

CW1
Gary Blanchard, MA, LADC1

Relapse is More Than Drug Use

You may think that relapse means that you have returned to drug use after stopping your use of drugs and alcohol. This is really only part of a relapse, and it is the final part of the relapse. To better understand this, think about how you were when you were addicted. You did things that you would not think of doing when you are not using. Perhaps you lied, both to yourself and to others. You might have taken money or sold things from around the house. Maybe you hung around people who were not good people to be around. Think about your activities when you were using. All of these things were a part of your addiction.

Once you start to work on your recovery you began to change these actions and people. At first, it may seem difficult, but you work hard at these changes. Soon, you stop paying attention to them. For a while everything is going well. Then, even though you do not notice it, you start to return to old habits or old people. This is a sign that you are in the process of relapse. If you do not recognize this and change your actions, it may not be long before you return to drug use.

By learning to recognize all the ways that addiction affected your life you can begin to recognize when your recovery begins to suffer. This allows you to stop a relapse before it leads to drug use and allows you to continue to build a successful recovery.

Recovery Is A Process

When you decide that it is time to eliminate alcohol and other drugs from your life, you want to put them down and have your life become magically normal. Unfortunately, this does not happen. In truth, the early months of the recovery process can be quite trying. You may suffer from Post-Acute Withdrawal, commonly referred to as PAW. While many are familiar with the acute withdrawal symptoms that are associated with some drugs, people are often unaware that there is another process that is going on in the brain and body when people stop using.

Since mood-altering chemicals mimic natural brain chemicals, your system becomes unbalanced when you flood it from drug use. The time it takes for your body and brain to readjust from using is considered PAW. During this period, you may experience mood swings, intense depression, lack of energy or motivation, sleep difficulties or a number of other symptoms. You need to recognize that these are normal and will lessen with time. Unfortunately, many people become impatient with the healing process and revert back to drug use to feel better.

Another part of the recovery process is becoming aware of the effect that your addiction had on your thoughts and behaviors. You need to determine how your thinking and actions were affected and eliminate the negative thoughts and behaviors while you replace them with positive ones. This takes time and work.

You will not become the person you want to be overnight; change takes time. As long as you are in the process and are moving forward, where you are today is okay for today. You need to be patient with the process.

CW2
Gary Blanchard, MA, LADC1

**Eight Common Tasks
of Positive Path Recovery**

1) Recognizing the need to change and committing to the work of recovery.

2) Redefining and rebuilding the sense of self. (The true self)

3) Taking responsibility and accepting forgiveness for past actions.

4) Learning to identify and express feelings.

5) Improving communication with others.

6) Restoring connection with significant people and making connection with others who can support recovery.

7) Identifying barriers to recovery and planning to overcome them.

8) Letting go!

CW3
Gary Blanchard, MA, LADC1

Task #1 Recognizing the need to change and committing to the work of recovery.

An old saying states that every journey begins with a single step. The Positive Path begins when a person admits that they have lost control over their use of mood-altering substances. As we have seen, sometimes it is not easy to make this admission. Once you have made it, however, you are on your way to recovery.

At this point I would like to state that, while an admission of the problem is essential, I feel it is possible to acknowledge it in an affirming manner. Generally, a person in recovery identifies himself or herself by saying "I am an alcoholic" or "I am an addict." I feel that it is much healthier to say, "I am a person who is recovering from addiction." This statement acknowledges the problem, but it also acknowledges that the person is in the process of change. This is a move away from self-denigration to self-affirmation. Since low self-esteem is common among people with addictive disease, you should affirm yourself as much as possible. This is not denial—it is admitting the truth in a positive way.

The second part of this task suggests a commitment to a path of recovery. It is important to realize that a commitment to recovery is the beginning of the recovery process rather than a one-time event. Once you have made this commitment, you are ready to recover the true self, the essence of your being. This will be discussed in detail in the exploration of the second task.

The commitment to a recovery path can seem overwhelming to some people. After years of relationship with their drug (or drugs) of choice some people feel they cannot think of life without it. The key is not to think of a lifetime of abstinence; break it down into smaller, more manageable time frames. A popular phrase in recovery is "One day at a time." This is an excellent advice. By telling yourself, "Today, I will refrain from using any and all mood-altering substances;" you have set a short-term goal that is easily reached. At first, you may find that you need to break it down into even smaller time frames. As time goes on, you may find that you expand the time frame. After a while, you may even find that you do not think about it at all.

I would like to point out that a commitment to recovery does not mean that you should not take prescribed medications. There are those who may need anti-depressants or other medication for psychological problems. These should be taken under medical supervision. Keep in mind that some of these medications may be addictive. Always tell your doctor about your history of addiction; the doctor can then prescribe medications that may be effective without the risk of addiction. Admitting that the drug has taken control of your life and committing, on a day by day basis if necessary, to recovery is the beginning of your journey of recovery. Here are some questions that might help you in this process:

What are some ways that your addiction has taken control of your life?

How have you tried to take control of your addiction?

Do you plan to commit to a path or recovery?

What are you doing to overcome your addiction?

CW4
Gary Blanchard, MA, LADC1

Task #2 Redefining and rebuilding the sense of self. (The true self)

The process of addiction is a slow, steady erosion of your sense of who you are. This process may very well start you begin drug or alcohol use. While addiction may be a genetic, biological disease, at times the erosion of the self may lead to the first use of our drug of choice. Other times the use of drugs leads to this erosion. Either way, I believe that disconnection from the true self is an outcome of addiction.

Before I define the true self, it is important to understand what is meant by the term "self." In common usage, the self is actually the self-concept, the way that a person views his or her self. The self-concept has three components. The first is the physical self, which is the basis of self-concept for newborn infants. The second component is the social self, which is based on the feedback that we get from other people. This is the way that other people see us. The third component is the true self, which should be the main component of the self-concept.

What is the true self? It is the purest essence of our being. It is what makes each of us unique and wonderful. When we first enter the world, we are purely ourselves. As we go through life, our experiences influence our thoughts and behavior.

We may try to conform to the needs and expectations of family and friends, the social self. This causes an uneasy feeling. Some people are aware of the problem and can deal with it; others try to hide from the feeling. When we hide from this uneasy feeling, a part of our true self is displaced.

Substance abuse is one way that people try to hide from the upset in their life. They find at first that the effect of the substance counteracts the uneasy feeling. Eventually, however, the substance will only add to it. The more they use, the more they will need to use. In the process, the physical self and the social self become the primary components of the self-concept. Recovery involves restoring the true self as the main part of the self-concept.

How can you redefine and rebuild your sense of self? One way is to spend some time in self-examination. The following questions can help you.

What do I believe about myself?

What do I believe about others?

What do I believe about the world around me?

What is important to me?

What moral or ethical guidelines do I feel that I must follow?

What must I have in order to feel fulfilled and at peace?

What do I want from life for myself and for others?

The answers to these questions will help reveal your true self. Another way to redefine and reconnect with the true self is through evaluating your strengths and weaknesses. Many times, a person who is addicted will lose track of these. They tend to overlook what is right about themselves and will overemphasize or deny what is wrong. You need to acknowledge both so that you have a balanced view of who you are. List as many of your strengths and weaknesses as possible. Feel free to add to these lists at a later time.

My strengths are:

My weaknesses are:

There are other techniques that you can use as well. Meditation is an effective way to help redefine and rebuild the true self. While meditation is used by many religions, it is not necessarily a "religious" technique. The purpose of meditation in many religions is to transcend the self; here it is used to more fully connect with the self.

While there is no special way that a person should meditate, there are things you can do to make it easier. First, you should get away, as much as possible, from distractions. Since it is difficult to find pure silence in everyday life, you may want to listen to some quiet music or a recording of the ocean or another natural sound to help overcome the other noises. Allow yourself to be comfortable; it does not matter if you are sitting up or lying down.

Gently allow your thoughts to slow. If you find that you are thinking about everyday problems, make note of it and then try to set them aside. If thoughts of these problems are persistent, then allow yourself to choose one and examine it. You may need to address some of these problems before you are able to connect more deeply with yourself. If you are able to get beyond these everyday worries, you may find that your "inner voice" becomes audible.

We all have thoughts and messages that rest in the unconscious mind. Many times, we react to them without knowing that they are there. In this type of meditation, you can allow these messages to move toward your consciousness. Sometimes these messages are affirming, other times they are destructive. We will look at ways of dealing with the destructive messages as we explore task #4. For now, simply let yourself be aware of these thoughts and messages.

Guided visualization is another technique that can help you to reconnect with the true self. The following visualization is a centering exercise that allows you to imagine yourself making a journey into the deeper recesses of the self. Playing quiet, relaxing music can help to make this exercise more effective. You may want to quietly lead yourself through this exercise, or you may find it better to record the exercise ahead of time. I have indicated spaces where you may want to pause to allow yourself time for reflection and revelation.

Close your eyes, find a comfortable position, and begin to connect with the pattern of your breathing. (Pause) As you breathe in and out, imagine that the rhythm of your breathing is the rhythm of life. (Pause) Imagine that you are standing at the beginning of a path that leads into a deep forest, the sun is shining down through the trees, creating a pattern of light and shadow on the grassy path ahead. (Pause) At the end of the path, you can see a bright light; this is the light of the sun illuminating a beautiful garden that is in the center of the woods. (Pause) As you continue to connect with your breath, the Earth's heartbeat, begin to travel down the path, taking time to notice the beauty that surrounds you. (Pause) As you travel this path, you hear the sound of a rippling stream, distant at first, but becoming louder as you continue walking. (Pause) As you travel this path, appreciating the beauty that surrounds you, you may find obstacles that impede your progress. Take note of these obstacles, knowing that they may slow your journey; you also know that they will not prevent you from continuing on the path to your destination. (Pause) After you have identified these obstacles, move past them and continue 22 CW4 Gary Blanchard, MA, LADC1 down the path, realizing that the encountering and bypassing the obstacle has brought you closer to the clearing at the center of the forest. (Pause) You slowly approach that clearing; the warmth of the sunlight brings a sense of comfort and connection to your heart and soul. Relax in the sunlight, rejoicing in its restorative power. (Pause) Kneel at the side of the stream; notice how clear and soothing the water is. (Pause) As you look into the stream, you see a reflection of yourself; this reflection shows the beauty that is reflected from your depth. (Pause) You sit by the stream, looking at the reflection; you are filled by the warmth of the sun and by the knowledge and awareness of your inner beauty. (Pause) When you are ready, slowly move back to the path, returning to the place where you began this trip. (Pause) As you continue your return trip, you will once again pass the obstacles that you encountered earlier; make note of them, knowing that they are not as powerful now as they were when you first encountered them. (Pause) As you approach the head of the path, you once again become aware of the pattern of your breathing. (Pause) Very slowly and gently open your eyes, allowing yourself to return to the present reality.

These techniques require practice, but they are effective ways of redefining and reconnecting with the true self. Again, remember that recovery is a process rather than an event.

CW5
Gary Blanchard, MA, LADC1

Task #3 Taking responsibility and accepting forgiveness for past actions.

Addiction is selfish by nature. The more a person needs their substance, the less they care about anything, or anyone, else. Once the process of recovery starts, a person must repair the damage that they have done during their active addiction. Taking responsibility may not erase the hurt and pain that others have felt, but it can ease that hurt and pain while it allows people to work toward better communication. Taking responsibility for past actions is more than just saying, "I'm sorry." Taking responsibility includes taking action to right those wrongs whenever possible. In addictions treatment an emphasis is placed on "making amends." This is a vital part of the recovery process. When you actively work at correcting the wrong you have done, you are strengthening your connection to the true self. Others are healed as you heal yourself.

How can you know who you have harmed and how can you repair the damage? In some cases, you are quite aware of the damage you inflicted while in active addiction. You see the hurt in the faces of family and significant people in your life. In other cases, the hurt may be less obvious. The best way to determine the extent of the damage is by having heartfelt talks with people. Explain that you were often unaware of what happened while you were in active addiction and that you want to know how your addiction affected the person. Most importantly, be ready and willing to listen to what the person has to say.

Listening to their answer may be difficult. You may not want to hear how awful you have been. An overactive sense of guilt may send you into a cycle of self-hatred. As we explore the fourth task, we will look at a way to overcome the self-talk that can prevent you from hearing what the person has to say.

You also need to ask what you can do to try to repair the damage. Your idea of appropriate action may be different from what the other person feels would be appropriate. To be effective, you need to meet the needs of the person that you have harmed.

Once you take responsibility for your actions, you must also accept forgiveness for them. The person that has been wrong may or may not offer forgiveness. Either way, you must forgive yourself. You cannot move forward if you are facing backwards. If you hold on to the guilt and shame, you will delay the recovery process. As you were actively addicted, you probably began to store a reservoir of guilt and shame. These feelings then fed your addiction. If you began to experience them, you would turn to the substance to block them. If you hold on to that guilt and shame in recovery, you increase the likelihood that you will return to active use of substances.

On a sheet of paper, or in a journal, list some of the actions that you need to take responsibility for and list ways that you can try to correct these actions. This will allow you to practice the art of accepting responsibility and forgiveness.

I take responsibility for:

I can try to correct this by:

Task #4 Learning to identify and express feelings.

As a person gets deeper into addiction, the main thing they consciously respond to is their drug. Feelings can get pushed aside; eventually they can wither and die. Once a person stops using chemicals, their feelings return; these feelings are often made stronger by physical or psychological withdrawal. As a person in recovery, you need to be able to recognize what you are feeling and need to be able to respond appropriately to these feelings. Sometimes you may be very aware of your feelings but find that you do not know how to express them in an appropriate manner. At other times you may find that you are completely numb. The awareness and expression of feelings is an important part of the recovery process.

People are generally able to identify categories of feelings, such as fear, sadness, surprise, and joy. There are differing degrees and types of each of these feelings. The more accurately you can identify your feeling, the better you can respond appropriately to it. There is a list of over one hundred feelings in the rear of the book that you can refer to. This list can help you learn how to identify your feelings more accurately.

One reason that people do not respond appropriately to feelings is that they may feel that some of those feelings are "bad" or "wrong." They may have been taught that anger is bad; therefore, they try to deny their anger. They may have learned that happiness is not acceptable in their family and so they try to hide or deny that feeling. It is important to understand that feelings are not good or bad; they are simply what they are.

It is interesting that in Spanish a person does not say, "I am sad;" instead, they say, "I have sadness." While it is important to identify and accept feelings, you can also see the feeling as something you "have" rather than see it as a means of personal identification. You can say "I have anger" instead of saying "I am angry."

Another part of the process of identifying and expressing feelings is recognizing negative self-talk. Many people in recovery have irrational messages that affect their self-image. These may have existed before the onset of addiction or they may be a result of chemical use. These messages often prevent a person from reacting to the reality of a situation. The best indication of the existence of these messages is your behavior. If you find yourself reacting in a way that seems inappropriate to the situation or having a reaction that is out of proportion to the "triggering event," you can be sure that there is a hidden, negative message that is affecting your actions.

Albert Ellis, a founder of the cognitive-behavioral theory of psychology, believed that many behaviors that are considered inappropriate are caused by irrational negative messages that the person received in their life. He developed an "A-B-C" theory of behavior that can be viewed in the following diagram:

$$A \rightarrow \qquad B \leftarrow \qquad \rightarrow C$$
(activating event)   (belief)   (consequence)

In this diagram, A is the event that eventually leads to C, the consequence of the event. The event, however, does not directly provide the consequence. It is the belief (B) about the event that causes the emotional or behavioral consequence. I do not want to overwhelm you with psychological theory, but the theory presented by Ellis does play a major part in repairing our separation from the true self.

Let me present an example of how this theory is displayed in a "real life" situation. Let us imagine that you are talking with someone who says, "I have been hurt by your actions while you were using drugs." You pull away and become angry or hurt. You are not reacting to their statement; you are reacting to deep-seated beliefs, perhaps that you are worthless and unlovable. Therefore, you react in an inappropriate manner. The problem is not that the person does not love you; the problem is that you do not love yourself.

A major part of identifying and expressing feelings is recognizing the underlying beliefs from your past that affect your emotions and behaviors. These beliefs affect you, no matter how deeply

170

they are buried. You must bring them into conscious awareness so you can eliminate their power. At first, these messages elude your consciousness. You will find yourself reacting to them without being aware of their existence.

The best way to bring them into awareness is to spend time evaluating an interaction after it is over. If you or another person feels that your reaction was inappropriate, spend some time in self-examination. Ask yourself what you were thinking when you reacted. Then compare those thoughts to the event that triggered the reaction. Do the thoughts agree with the triggering event? If not, where might they have come from? How often do you have these thoughts that affected your reaction? You may be surprised at first how often your behavior is affected by underlying beliefs rather than by actual events. As you increase your awareness of these beliefs, you will probably find that they are major hindrance to your path of recovery. I want to remind you that you should not be discouraged by the discoveries that you are making at this point.

Ellis developed an approach to disputing these messages that he called Rational Emotive Behavior Therapy (REBT). Below is an expansion of the earlier diagram, showing the REBT process:

$A \rightarrow$ B $\rightarrow C$
(activating event)   (belief)   (consequence)
$\downarrow$
D $\rightarrow E$ $\rightarrow F$
(disputing intervention)   (new effect) (new feeling)

In this diagram, "D" is the disputing intervention; a three-step process designed to challenge the irrational beliefs. The first step in this process is detecting the irrational beliefs; especially "shoulds," "musts," "awfulizing," and "self-downing." The second part is debating these beliefs by learning how to logically question them and effectively learn to act against believing them. The third step is to learn to discriminate irrational beliefs from rational beliefs. As you learn to use the disputing intervention, you arrive at "E," an effective, rational philosophy. This philosophy helps create "F," a new set of feelings.

I know from personal experience how powerful these irrational negative messages can be. I have often found myself feeling completely hopeless and unlovable because of these messages; many times I have reacted to these messages instead of reality. I have been applying the disputing intervention to these messages and have found that they lose power with each intervention. I still have these messages, but I am learning more and more to recognize them as the irrational beliefs that they are. The use of REBT is one of the most effective tools that I have found for recovering self-esteem and eliminating irrational reactions.

The following exercise allows you to evaluate interactions to determine the belief that led to the consequence and to develop ways to dispute the belief. This format can be copied and used to evaluate any interaction that seems to be affected by hidden irrational beliefs.

Describe an event where you feel you had an inappropriate response:

What are the beliefs that you may have reacted to?

How can you dispute those beliefs?

You also need to learn how to better identify what you are feeling. There are many levels of feeling and it is good to find the best way to describe it. You may say that you feel sad; this could be anything from feeling somewhat down to feeling hopeless. When you are more accurate in your description of your feelings, you are better able to express them in an appropriate manner. Try to find words that describe levels of the following feelings:

Happy
Sad
Mad
Hurt

It is also good to recognize that feelings may sometimes be the result of feeling several things at the same time. For instance, anger may be a combination of feeling hurt, sad, disappointed, and disrespected. Select a feeling that you often feel and use a feeling list to try to determine other related feelings that may be involved.

I often feel:

Some related feelings may be:

Task #5 Improving communication
with others

The fifth task is improving communication with others. It is ironic that people under the influence often consider themselves to be great communicators. Many people will state that relatives or friends have recorded their speech while they were under the influence; each will relate, with some surprise and embarrassment, that they did not realize how meaningless and inarticulate they were at the time. They actually thought they were being charming and intelligent.

Many times, people with addiction problems were afraid of communicating honestly prior to the onset of their addiction. Once they give up their drug of choice they find that it is harder than they realized to talk to others, yet they also find that they need to talk with others in order to support recovery. They need to have faith in themselves and to trust that others will hear what they have to say. Rediscovering, or in many cases discovering for the first time, how to communicate with others is vitally important to maintaining sobriety.

Communication is an important part of any relationship. Effective communication requires listening skills as well as speaking skills. Before you can listen to others, however, you must be able to listen to yourself.

Many people feel that self-awareness is a selfish thing. In reality, it is vital to any type of interaction in life. Your relationship to other people, to nature, and to society is affected by your ability to know and to accept yourself.

We examined the effects of subconscious, irrational messages in the examination of the fourth task. These messages are a major hindrance to any type of communication. The example in that chapter demonstrated how these messages affect your listening; you may hear and react to echoes from the past rather than the voice of the present. Recognizing these messages and their effects are part of the communication process.

As you can recognize these messages and the effect that they have, you will be increasingly able to communicate from a space beyond the effect of those messages. In some cases, it may be that you can tell the person that you are reacting to "flashes from the past;" in other cases, you may need to be able to move yourself to a space beyond those messages, or to adjust your reaction in a way that negates the power of the message. Again, the REBT process is an excellent way to deal with these situations.

Can you think of some situations when you may have reacted to what you thought was said instead of what was said? What could you do differently to keep this from happening again?

If you have grown up to be afraid of your feelings, you may find it difficult to admit your feelings to yourself and to other people. This inability to face your feelings can be a major hindrance for communication in relationships. If, for instance, I am afraid of being rejected, I may find it difficult to express my needs to another person. In order to avoid having to share my needs and face rejection, I suppress the need, trying to pretend that it is not there. This denial does not eliminate that need; it will surface somehow. An unexpressed and unacknowledged need, however, often reveals itself in a less than desirable fashion. It is far better to learn to express your feelings and needs than to repress them. An unexpressed need that reveals itself through inappropriate behavior causes problems that must then be discussed; the behavior adds to the problem.

You should also be aware that other people may have buried messages, and that they may or may not be aware of them. If communication is a problem, look at interactions in the relationship to see if the other person seems to be reacting to something other than the current conversation. If so, let the nature of the relationship decide your reaction to the situation. In an intimate relationship, you may want to point out that the person seems to be reacting to something other than the present situation. In less intimate relationships, it may be necessary to make allowances for the person's actions.

Cultural differences can also affect communication style and understandings. While men and women may not be from separate planets, their social training is usually different. Women may be raised to value specific traits, such as openness and vulnerability; men are often taught that these traits are signs of weakness. Racial, economic, and social differences can also result in differing values and understandings. When communication in a relationship seems blocked, it may be the result of such differences. Again, in a more intimate relationship, or in a necessary relationship, it is important for the people involved to talk about these issues and to try to come to mutual understanding. In more superficial relationships, it may be best to make allowances and try to move on.

There are ways to improve communication. One is to stay as positive as the situation permits. Avoid name-calling, sarcasm, threats, and intimidation. If you are talking about a behavior you do not like, attack the behavior, not the person. When possible, offer suggestions for solutions to a problem. Use the "sandwich" method when presenting information that could be perceived as negative; say something positive, offer the correction, then follow it with a positive statement. For example, you might say, "You have been very supportive of my recovery. I wish you could be more patient with my progress. I know you are doing your best to be understanding."

Using the techniques listed above, try to find a better way to say the following?

You are just a nag.

Do you want to call me that again? Are you ready for the consequence?

I wish you would stop leaving things around the house.

It makes me mad that you do not trust me.

Another way to improve communication is by being clear and specific. Make your point clearly; ask for what you want and tell how you feel. Avoid saying that a person "always" or "never" does something. If you are going to quote what someone said, be accurate. If you are talking about someone's actions, give specific times and examples. Avoid exaggeration, and stick to what is relevant.

It is important to talk from your own point of view. Avoid saying things like, "You just think that..." or "You just wanted to..." as these statements assume knowledge of the other person's feelings and motives. Own your feelings; avoid saying things like, "You made me sad." Use "I" messages, for example, "I feel sad when I think you are mad at me." Also, avoid saying things like, "I know how you feel." Try to change the following to "I" messages:

You do that to get on my nerves.

You are always nagging me. I would do better if you stopped nagging.

It is also important to keep communication a two-way process. Do not monopolize; allow the other person a chance to respond while they can remember what is on their mind. Ask for feedback, for example, "Please tell me what you understood me to say." If the person did not understand, it allows you to rephrase the statement in a way that insures understanding.

Another aid to good communication is to stay on the subject. If possible, organize your thoughts ahead of time. Discuss one topic at a time and do not bring up issues that are already settled. Also, avoid "kitchen sinking," bringing up every problem and issue at one time.

Finally, good listening is an important part of communication. Give the person your full attention rather than rehearsing what you are going to say next. Let your posture, tone, and expression indicate that you are listening. Do not interrupt the person. If you are not sure you understand what the person said, ask them to clarify it. Paraphrase what they said and ask if that is correct. If not, ask then to restate it.

Good communication is essential part of recovery, and will also be helpful as we prepare to examine the next task of the Positive Path.

Task#6: Restoring connection with significant people and making connection with others who can support recovery.

Some relationships may have become strained while you were in active addiction; others may have been damaged beyond repair. It is important to try to restore those that you can and be able to let go of the ones that you cannot. There will be some relationships that you will not want to maintain in recovery, as they may be harmful to your sobriety.

Family relationships are very important. These should be your first priority. You should be aware, however, that people close to you might have lost trust as a result of your past actions. As much as they might want to believe that things will be different, they are all too aware of past promises of sobriety. It may take time to restore the trust that is needed for intimacy. Be patient, and let your actions speak for you.

There may be friends that have fallen away from you during your active addiction. These people may have cared about you but they slowly became frustrated with your continued use of drugs or alcohol. You need to contact these people to apologize for any harm that you caused them in the past; let them know that you are now working on your recovery and that you would appreciate

180

their support and friendship. Some people may not be able or willing to renew the friendship; you should be prepared for this. Others however may be glad to restore their friendship and to support your recovery. As I mentioned earlier, some friendships have been based upon our addictive use of substances; these relationships are best abandoned.

Relationships with supervisors and coworkers may have also suffered as a result of your drug use. Again, the best approach is to apologize for the damage that was caused by your use and to ask for their support of your recovery.

Take some time to reflect on the important relationships in your life. Use the following categories to make a list:

Relationships that are important to my recovery:

Relationships I would like to continue if possible:

Relationships that can hurt my recovery:

In addition to restoring important existing relationships, you also need to connect with new people who can support recovery. I feel that 12 step meetings, such as Alcoholics Anonymous (AA) or Narcotics Anonymous (NA), can be an excellent source of support for recovery. While some people in these meetings tend to be very dogmatic about the program, many wonderful people attend these meetings; people who are committed to attaining and maintaining sobriety.

Many twelve-step groups also sponsor social functions such as dances and coffeehouses that offer a sober social environment. Other sources of support include Celebrate Recovery, Dharma Recovery and SMART Recovery.

You can also find new relationships through special interest groups, such as writer's groups, through churches, places like the Ethical Society, social actions groups, and other similar organizations. It is important to remember, however, that people in these groups may be social (or addicted) users of alcohol or other drugs. Do not put yourself in a situation that could lead to a return to use. (This will be explored further in the next chapter.)

As you work on restoring and making connections with others you will find the easiest way to approach any relationship is to treat others in the same way that you would want to be treated. The hardest way may be to treat others in the way they would want to be treated. You should try to do both. Respect people who have differing points of view, even if you cannot agree with them. By listening to the feelings and needs of others, we learn more about others as well as ourselves.

Task #7 Identifing barriers to recovery and planning to overcome them.

In the very first task we talked about committing to recovery. This is, of course, much easier to say than to do. Tasks two through six deal with ways to sustain recovery and promote self-awareness and personal growth. In addition to the skills gained in those principles, you need to recognize specific situations that could tempt you to return to alcohol or drug use.

As stated earlier in this book, a return to drug use after a period of sobriety is often referred to as a relapse, suggesting that the disease has again become active. There are several things that I feel you need to understand as we look at the issue of relapse.

First, you should recognize that relapse is possible but should also understand that it is not inevitable. In other words, you should be aware of the possibility but should not obsess about it. When you concentrate too much on relapse, you can mentally set yourself up for failure. When you concentrate on recovery, you maintain a positive focus; if you concentrate on relapse, you have a negative focus.

Secondly, you should be aware of the difference between a relapse and a slip. A slip is a one-time use of a mood-altering chemical. The obvious danger is that it can lead to a full return to addictive use. The important word in the last sentence is "can." A slip does not have to develop into a relapse. If you begin to blame and shame yourself for a slip, you can set yourself up for a full relapse. If, however, you can tell yourself that it was an error in judgment that you do not want to repeat, you have a better chance of getting quickly back on track. When looking at barriers to recovery, often referred to as relapse triggers, the common list is "people, places, and things." The following exercises will look at ways to identify these various barriers and to help you develop ways to deal with them.

People

Some of the people who play a significant role in your life are people who also use mood-altering substances. It is difficult to maintain abstinence when you are around others who are using drugs or alcohol. It is too easy to be drawn back into use, especially during the early recovery period. Very often, people who are still using drugs or alcohol feel threatened by your sobriety and will encourage you to return to use. These people may be friends, family, or coworkers. You can separate yourself from some of these people; others may play an important role in your life, such as spouses, relatives, and co-workers. Work on the following exercise to help you to look at the people in your life who use mood-altering substances and to evaluate how to deal with them.

List all people who use mood-altering substances and who play a significant role in your life:

List those who can be avoided or eliminated from your life:

List those who you cannot avoid or eliminate:

How can you adjust your relationship with them to prevent them from hurting your recovery?

Who are positive people who can support your recovery?

Places

There may be places that had a significant role in your use of drugs or alcohol. Some may be obvious, such as bars and clubs; others may have more subtle associations, such as school, work, or other places where you often used mood-altering substances. Some may be easy to stay away from, others may not. The following questions will help you to determine places that may affect your recovery and to think of ways to deal with them.

What places do you associate with alcohol or drug use?

Which of these places can you easily stay away from?

Which of these places cannot be avoided?

What can you do to maintain your recovery while you are in these places?

What are new places that will support your recovery?

Things

There are many "things" that can possibly lead to relapse. There may be sounds or smells that you associate with our use of substances. There may be situations that will make you crave the high you got from your drug. There may be feelings that are strongly associated with using drugs. These are the things that can threaten your sobriety if you are not prepared for them.

What situations usually accompanied drug use?

Are there sights, sounds, or other things that make you think of drugs?

Choose several of these and develop ways to deal with them. (Avoidance, building new associations or reactions, etc.)

What are new things you can add to your life to support recovery?

Attitudes and Beliefs

While people, places, and things are frequently identified as relapse triggers, I feel that attitudes and beliefs are perhaps the biggest obstacles that a person in recovery must overcome. As I have stated before, behaviors are affected by feelings and feelings are affected by what we think. There are a number of ways that attitudes and belief can make a person vulnerable to relapse. In each case, I will present the attitude or belief as well as ways to dispute them. I would like to acknowledge that some of the information here is found in the book, Rational Emotive Therapy with Alcoholics and Substance Abusers, by Albert Ellis, et al. Again, it is important to remember that it takes time to overcome these old beliefs. Be patient with yourself and the process.

If you have the attitude that abstinence from drugs and alcohol is a curse, you will find that recovery is a burden and you will quickly return to using. If, on the other hand, you decide that abstinence is an opportunity to improve your life you will find that recovery is much easier. If you find yourself faced with this attitude, tell yourself that you are making a choice to improve the quality of your life and you do not need mood-altering substances in your new life. Another attitudinal barrier to recovery is self-pity. If you feel sorry for yourself because other people can use substances "responsibly" and you cannot, you may decide it is all too unfair and you are going to use no matter what the consequences may be. This happens more often than you may imagine. If this is happening to you, you may tell yourself that other people do a lot of things that you cannot do, but that what matters is all the things that you are able to do, including living a clean and sober life. Some people will think, "Drinking and/or using drugs isn't a problem for me. It's other people who have a problem with the way I drink and use." The way to combat that is to tell yourself "If my drinking or using is a problem for others, it soon will be for me if it is not already a problem."

Another common attitude is that sobriety will be too hard, and you might lose your friends, be bored, or be uncomfortable. To combat this attitude, remind yourself that while it may take some time and effort, you may lose much more if you continue to use.

Feeling as though you cannot stand to not have another drink or drug is another common attitude that can hurt recovery. You need to admit to yourself that abstinence is difficult, but you have endured other difficulties in the past. Also remind yourself that while you may want another drink or drug, you do not need to have it. On a sheet of paper, in this book, or in a journal, identify some of the attitudes that may impede your recovery and lead to relapse, then develop a way to dispute the attitudes. Take time to consider both the attitudes and possible ways that you can dispute them.

My attitude:

How I can dispute that attitude:

CW10
Gary Blanchard, MA, LADC1

Task #8 Letting Go!

The final task consists of two simple words that carry a lot of meaning. What does it mean to let go and what are you letting go?

To begin with, you are learning to let go of feelings of guilt and shame that trap you in your addictive behavior. By taking responsibility for your actions and accepting forgiveness for them, you can release any guilt and shame. The past becomes the past and you can live in the present moment—free from any mood-altering substances.

You also let go of the compulsive desire to control the uncontrollable and to change the unchangeable. To paraphrase a familiar recovery saying, you accept what you cannot change, change what you can, and you learn to understand the difference. You cannot change what other people do, for instance, but you can change how you react to it.

You also let go of judgment of yourself and others. You learn to accept yourself as you are, at this moment, knowing that you are on the path of recovery.

Finally, you let go of identifying yourself with your addiction. The focus changes from "what I was" to "what I am." After years of sobriety, once the craving has been quieted, the recovering person can close the door on the past. This is not saying that a person can return to "responsible using;" in most cases any use at all could quickly lead to a full relapse. What is recommended is that the person build an identity that no longer needs their drug of choice as an identifier. This is the process of removing the drug from the self-concept.

What do you need to "Let Go" to improve your life and your recovery?

What can you do to make this happen?

CW11
Gary Blanchard, MA, LADC1

Practicing Patience

I have often heard it said that addiction is a disease of impatience, and I certainly must agree. There is the desire for instant gratification that helps the disease to progress. If people needed to wait a long period of time to feel the effect of a drink or drug, chances are they may never have done enough of it to get addicted. It is the sudden mood swing that grabs a person and keeps them coming back. After they become hooked on this mood swing, it is hard to be patient with the process of recovery.

I often tell folks that addiction, like recovery, is a process. The difference is that the process of addiction starts out as fun and becomes work, while the process of recovery starts out as work and becomes fun. As discussed in the previous chapter, in the early stages of recovery you face Post-Acute Withdrawal as well as other consequences of your addiction such as financial, legal, and relationship problems. These relationships may be family, work, or other relationships. As you face these problems in early recovery, you want the same instant relief from them that the drug provided. Unfortunately, there is no instant relief. By definition, a process takes time. You need to learn to take the time and let things grow and build.

I would like to point out that impatience is not limited to addiction; ours is an impatient society. I remember, when I was a kid, that to get a paper from my home on the East Coast to California took time and effort. I would need to put it in an envelope, put a stamp on it, and take it to the mail box. Several days to a week later it would arrive in California. Now, I take that piece of paper to the fax machine, dial a number, press send and the information goes almost immediately to California. Yet, I stand there complaining that the fax machine is slow. If you combine the impatience of our society with the impatience of addiction, there is a lot to overcome.

The only "cure" for the problem is to re-train the mind to be patient. You need to remind yourself that many things do take time. You need to remember that anything worth having is worth waiting for. You need to practice patience. The more you work at it, the more patient you become.

I once read about the Prayer for Patience. This simple prayer states: "God, give me patience and give it to me now!" The absurdity of this makes me laugh; it also allows me to see the absurdity of my own impatience. Whenever I find my patience wearing thin, I remind myself of the Prayer for Patience.

How has a lack of patience affected your recovery?

Are there areas of your life that require more patience?

What can you do to become more patient?

CW12
Gary Blanchard, MA, LADC1

Progress, Not Perfection

There are many slogans in the Recovery Culture. Some of them are rather lame; others start to lose their meaning with constant repetition. There is, however, one slogan that has always been important to me. That slogan is the title of this chapter.

Recognizing the need to make progress rather than to achieve perfection is another way to learn patience. If your aim is perfection, then anything less than perfection is failure. This creates a pressure not only to become perfect, but to do it as quickly as possible, since every day you are not perfect is a day of failure. With this type of pressure, patience is impossible.

The key is to recognize the progress that you have made in your recovery. Each day of recovery brings improvement. Each day brings you closer to the end of Post-Acute Withdrawal. Each day, if you are working a recovery program, brings you closer to resolving the financial, legal, and relationship problems that were created by your addiction.

Sometimes you are not able to recognize your progress. You feel as though you are just spinning your wheels. This is when you need to stop and take a look back to see how far you have come in your recovery. Progress is sometimes so gradual that you do not recognize that it has added up to significant change.

Another way to keep track of progress is to have a person or persons that you trust as a source of information. You can use these people as a "mirror" to reflect back to you the changes you have made in your life. This is important, as it is hard to see yourself realistically. Your image of yourself is influenced by how you are thinking and feeling at the time. If you are depressed, you are likely to have a low self-image. If you are happy, you are more likely to have a higher self-image. Having someone who can serve as a mirror helps you to have a clearer view of your progress in recovery. When you recognize that you are making progress, you are more likely to continue building recovery.

It is important to recognize that there are times when you are in a "holding pattern." You are not moving forward but are not moving backward. This is natural, and should not be a cause of concern. There are times when you need to rest, when the changes you have made need to "settle in." As long as you are not moving backward, you are still making progress. If this happens for too long a period, however, you may want to look at what is going on in your life that is keeping you stuck.

How do you measure your progress?

Are there areas of your life that you would like to see progress?

CW13
Gary Blanchard, MA, LADC1

Staying Focused

We are constantly hearing that modern society has resulted in people with short attention spans. We tend to get easily distracted and find it difficult to keep our attention on any one thing for too long. While we could debate the reasons for this, I think that we really cannot debate that staying focused is harder to do in our current society. Add to this societal problem the fact that years of alcohol and drug use also affects your ability to concentrate and you can see that staying focused on recovery may be a challenge.

What can you do to stay focused? One easy thing is to "stay in the moment." It is so easy to start thinking ahead of the months and years that you will need to be alcohol and drug free that you then become focused on all the wrong things. Again, the adage, "One Day At A Time," is more than a cliché. I can more easily stay focused on what I am doing today than I can on what I will do ten years from now.

Another way to maintain focus is to stay aware of your goals and the rewards that come from meeting those goals. When that momentary thought of "why am I doing this" comes, being focused on what I am trying to achieve keeps me from getting off track.

Surrounding yourself with positive influences is another way to stay focused. When the people, places, and things in your life support recovery, you are better able to keep your focus on recovery. If, on the other hand, you keep yourself surrounded by negative influences, you are more likely to have your focus wander in the wrong direction.

Positive self-talk is another way that you can keep your focus. The first affirmation of the "New Life Acceptance Program," developed by Women for Sobriety, states, "I have a life-threatening problem that once had me." I like this, because it indicates taking charge of your life, and making change to allow this to continue. You also need to watch negative self-talk. I feel that the two most dangerous words in our language are "I can't." I do not feel that we can do anything, but I do believe that, once we tell ourselves we cannot do something, we have guaranteed that we cannot do it. There is one place, however, where you should use "I can't" in your recovery. You need to remember, "I can't ever use alcohol or drugs without causing more trouble in my life."

Gentle reminders of what you are trying to do in your life can also help you to stay focused. Some people may cover their car bumper with recovery stickers, some might have a copy of the Serenity Prayer hanging on the wall; others find more subtle, personal reminders. An AA token or NA keychain, hidden in a pocket, can be a great reminder to maintain focus.

Do you have trouble staying focused?

What tools can you use to keep focused?

CW14
Gary Blanchard, MA, LADC1

You Are Not Your Addiction

After years of active addiction, it is easy to believe that the addiction is who you are. The fact is, the addiction may control you, but it does not define you. If you can recognize this difference, it becomes easier to move away from the addiction.

How many times have you told yourself that you need (or want) your drug of choice, even though you really have made a decision to quit? While you have committed to recovery, there is something inside of you that seems to want to pull you down and back to active using. This is the addiction speaking to you. If you can recognize that this thought is not coming from you but from the addiction, it becomes easier to take action against that thought. Instead of thinking, "I want to use," the thought becomes "It wants to use." The next step is to ask yourself why you should give "It" what "It" wants.

Also, when you recognize that you are not your addiction, you realize that, while you are responsible for your actions, you acted not on your beliefs and values, but on the beliefs and values of the addiction. When you learn to separate yourself from your addiction, you gain control of your thoughts and actions. The exercises provided earlier help you to connect with the true self and disconnect from the addiction.

Do you have trouble separating yourself from your addiction?

If you do, what can you do to improve this?

If not, what is helping you to keep the separation?

CW15
Gary Blanchard, MA, LADC1

Understanding Triggers

If you have ever had any treatment for addiction, or have attended Twelve-Step meetings, you have heard of relapse triggers. These are things that activate the urge to use alcohol or other drugs. Some triggers are obvious, such as being around people who are using or going to places where you used to buy drugs. Some triggers are less obvious and can be unique to the person. To learn how to deal with a trigger, you need to have a better idea of how a trigger works.

You may have heard of the researcher Pavlov and his experiments with dogs. He would ring a bell every time he fed the dogs; the dogs would salivate when the food arrived. After time, the dogs would salivate when the bell rang, even if there was no food. The dogs became trained, or conditioned, to associate the bell with food. As a result, the sound of the bell was the same to them as the sight and smell of food.

A trigger is a reaction that you have created in your mind to a thing or event. As stated before, your triggers may be common ones, or they may be very unusual. The key to dealing with triggers is to identify them, then figure ways to deal with them.

Take time to list your triggers; things that make you think about drug use. Once you have identified them, start thinking about what you can do to deal them. Some can be easily avoided or eliminated. Others will take more work and effort.

We can look at triggers as equations. If, for instance, having money is a trigger for you, the equation would seem to read "M=U," or "Money equals Using." Yet, for many people, money is not a trigger for alcohol or drug use. The real equation is "M+B=U," or "Money plus my belief about Money equals Using." In other words, it is not the money that triggers your desire to use, but what you think or believe about the money that triggers the desire or craving. Once you understand this, a solution to dealing with this trigger is easily seen. Since money in a necessity that cannot be eliminated, you can instead change what you believe about money. Instead of thinking, "If I have money, I need to use drugs," you can think, "I can use this money to do something constructive in my life." This is another application of the REBT process discussed earlier in this book. Again, changing the thinking and belief about the trigger will take time and work, but the result makes the effort worthwhile.

Make a list of possible triggers you may face.

What beliefs are a part of these triggers?

Use the tools you have gained to determine ways to deal with these triggers.

CW16
Gary Blanchard, MA, LADC1

Problem Solving

Another way to deal with triggers is through problem solving. I had a teenage client who identified watching a particular television program as a trigger since he always smoked marijuana while the show was on. He did not feel that he could give up watching the show, as it was one of his favorites. While that was debatable, it provided an opportunity to demonstrate a problem-solving approach to dealing with a trigger.

We decided to present the problem to the group. The group then began to make suggestions. Some of these suggestions were rather strange, some would provide an outcome worse than the marijuana use, others, though, seemed possible. The final decision was that watching this program would become a family event; if he watched the show with his parents, he would not be able to smoke marijuana. He would also be able to talk to them about any cravings that he experienced. His parents agreed to this approach.

The difficulty with problem solving is that most addicted people used drugs and alcohol to escape problems and saw this as problem solving. Chances are that you lack problem-solving skills. The rest of this chapter will explore several problem-solving skills and tools.

One tool that was used in the example above is brainstorming. As the old saying goes, two heads are better than one. When you work alone for a solution, your experience, imagination, and abilities limit you. When other people join in the process, you get a wider range of experience, imagination and abilities.

In brainstorming, you have people suggest any idea that comes to them, no matter how silly or far out it may seem. All ideas are written down. Once the ideas are given, the group begins to look at them to decide if they are workable, if they will produce the desired result, and if the person is able to put the idea into action. Eventually, you will select the one that seems best to you and apply it. If there is more than one possible solution, it might be good to write down the others in case the selected solution does not work. Surprisingly, sometimes the solution that seemed far-out or silly will prove to be the best.

Often, a problem is difficult to face because it is too large and overwhelming. If, for instance, you are facing major financial problems, it may be too scary to look at the situation; therefore, you may just ignore it. A way to deal with this is to break the problem down. Make a list of all the debts. Then you can prioritize them. What is the most important one to deal with? What is less important? Are there any bills that you can eliminate? Anything you can give up to save money?

Another step is to take action. Continuing with the last example, you can call creditors to see if you can arrange for a payment plan. Some creditors are willing to work with you if you make an effort. Sometimes, talking to the creditor shows that you are taking responsibility; this lets them know that you are willing to make good on your obligation. Sometimes creditors might be able to suggest resources to get help with payments.

I know a person who has periodic bouts of depression. When he is in a major depressive episode he does not keep up with housework and his apartment becomes messy and disorganized. As the depression clears, he feels overwhelmed by the amount of work needed to get the house straight. He learned to break it down into smaller portions. One day he decides to clean a corner of one room. When he is done, he may decide that he is ready and able to work on another corner. On the other hand, he may decide that he has accomplished his goal for the day and then has a feeling of accomplishment. Within a reasonable amount of time, his apartment is back to normal. If he did not break the task down, however, chances are nothing would happen.

Another problem-solving tool is asking for help. This is hard for some people to do. Many people feel that asking for help is a sign of weakness or failure. Asking for help is really a normal and natural thing to do; I see it as a sign of strength and determination. We all have different skills and abilities. When you ask for help, you expand the resources that are available to you.   Sometimes, the hardest part of problem solving is deciding the right course of action. In recovery, you may face some tough decisions. You may need to consider whether to change jobs or may need to consider ending a significant relationship. Before you can decide how to solve the problem, you need to decide what the solution should be. A great tool for this is a decision grid.

To make a decision grid, take a piece of paper and draw lines to divide it into quarters. For this example, we will look at deciding whether to change jobs. In the top left grid, write "Advantages of Staying." In the top right, put "Disadvantages of Staying." The bottom left grid would be "Advantages of Changing" and the bottom right, "Disadvantages of Changing." Now that the grid is prepared, make a list of everything you can think of for each category. For most major decisions, I suggest that you return to it several times over a period of several days or longer. Each time you go over the list, see if you still agree with the things you listed and add to the list as you think of new things.   Now you are ready to look at the grid and evaluate the information. You may have several entries under one or two columns and have other columns with few entries. That might indicate what the proper decision would be. On the other hand, you have to consider the quality of entries as well as the quantity. This grid, however, should help you to determine your best choice.

List problems that you face in your recovery.

What can you do to solve them?

Have you asked for help or suggestions?

Use the Decision Grid to examine a decision in your life.

CW17
Gary Blanchard, MA, LADC1

Weakening Worry

Worry is a major barrier to problem solving and can be a trigger. Worry is natural, and, in moderation, moves people to take action. When worry is allowed to take over, however, it becomes a problem.

One night I was scrolling through the TV channels and came across a PBS program on the subject of worry. The person in that program defined worry as "obsessing over things that will probably never happen." Since I tended to worry a lot, I held on to that definition. When I evaluated all the times of worry that I could recall, I realized that 80% of the things I worried about did not happen; also, worry did not stop the other 20% from happening. It was then that I recognized that I should, and could, do something to lessen my worry.

In early recovery, there is a lot to worry about. You may be experiencing some physical problems. You may have financial difficulties. In addition, your personal relationships might be strained. With all of this to worry about, the thought of the escape that drug use offers is inviting. Rationally, you know this is not a solution, but addiction is not rational. What can you do to escape the worry without using drugs?
First, you need to remind yourself that worry will not eliminate the problem. Then you can look at

the causes of worry. The physical problems may be the result of Post-Acute Withdrawal (PAW), which was discussed in an earlier chapter. You will want to meet with a doctor to discuss your problems. It is important that your doctor know that you are in the early stages of recovery from addiction. The financial problems need to be faced using some of the problem-solving tools from the last chapter. The relationships will take work; you can use some of the communication tools from Chapter Nine to help; family counseling may also be needed.

The important thing to realize is worry will not relieve the situation and will only make it worse. You need to take action and then let go of the worry. This is not easy to do, but you can train yourself to do it.

Whenever I find myself starting to worry about something, I ask myself if I have begun work on changing the situation. If I have not, I need to start to do something about the situation. If I have, I then ask myself if there is anything that worrying about the situation will accomplish. If the answer to that is no, I make myself lay the situation aside.

I needed to learn to do this. I visualized putting the problem in a basket outside my door, telling myself I would pick it back up when I had the tools to deal with it. I also remind myself that, as long as I am doing something about the problem, worrying will not accomplish anything. With time,

I have become good at doing this. You can do the same.

What are things that cause you to worry?

Are you taking steps to deal with the sources of worry?

What can you do to ease your worry?

Bibliography

Alcoholics Anonymous World Services, Inc. (1976). *Alcoholics Anonymous*. New York: Author

American Psychiatric Association. (2000). *Diagnostic and Statistical Manual of Mental Disorders (Fourth Edition) Text Revision – DSM-IV- TR*. Washington, DC: Author

Beebe, S., Beebe, S., & Redmond, M. (1999) *Interpersonal Communication: Relating to Others*. Boston: Allyn & Bacon.

Corey, G. (1981). *Theory and Practice of Group Counseling*. Monterey, CA: Brooks/Cole Publishing Company.

DeVito, J. (1998). *The Interpersonal Communication Book*. New York: Longman

Ellis, A. & Harper, R. (1975). *A New Guide to Rational Living*. N. Hollywood: Wilshire Book Company.

Ellis, A., McInerney, J.F., DiGiuseppe, R., & Yeager, R.J. (1988). *Rational-Emotive Therapy with Alcoholics and Substance Abusers*. Boston: Allyn & Bacon.

Ellis, A. & Velton, E. (1992). *When AA Doesn't Work for You: Rational Steps to Quitting Alcohol*. Fort Lee, NJ: Barricade Books.

Fiorentine, R., & Anglin, M. (1997). Does Increasing the Opportunity for Counseling Increase the Effectiveness of Outpatient Drug Treatment? *American Journal of Drug and Alcohol Abuse 23*, 369-383. (Download from Norwich University Expanded Academic ASAP.)

Firman, J. & Gila, A. (1997). *The Primal Wound: A Transpersonal View of Trauma, Addiction, and Growth*. Albany: State University of New York Press.

Glasser, W. (1965). *Reality Therapy: A New Approach to Psychiatry*. New York: Harper and Row

Gorski, T. (1989). *How to Start Relapse Prevention Support Groups*. Independence, MO: Herald House/Independence Press.

Gorski, T. & Miller, M. (1982). *Counseling for Relapse Prevention*. Independence, MO: Herald House/Independence Press.

Grof, C. (1993). *The Thirst for Wholeness: Attachment, Addiction, and the Spiritual Path*. New York: HarperCollins Publisher.

Guilar, J. (2001). *The Interpersonal Communications Skill Workshop: A Trainer's Guide*. New York: American Management Association.

Kuhn, C., Swartzwelder, S., & Wilson, W. (1998). *Buzzed: The Straight Facts About the Most Used and Abused Drugs from Alcohol to Ecstasy.* New York: W. W. Norton & Company.

Miller, W et al (1999). *Enhancing Motivation for Change in Substance Abuse Treatment.* Washington, DC: SAMSHA

Mueller, L. & Ketcham, K. (1987). *Recovering: How to Get and Stay Sober.* New York: Bantam Books

Nakken, C. (1988). *The Addictive Personality: Understanding Compulsion in Our Lives.* New York: HarperCollins Publisher.

National Institute on Drug Abuse (NIDA). (2000). *Principles of Drug Addiction Treatment: A Research Based Guide.* Washington, D.C.: Author

O'Brien, C. (1997). A Range of Research-Based Pharmacotherapies for Addiction. *Science, 278*(5335), 66-71. (Download from Norwich University Expanded Academic ASAP.)

Pita, D. (1992). *Addictions Counseling.* New York: Crossroad Publishing

Rogers, C. (1961). *On Becoming a Person.* Boston: Houghton Mifflin Company

Sawrey, J. & Telford, C. (1971). *Psychology of Adjustment.* Boston: Allyn and Bacon

Scott, C (2000). Ethical Issues in Addiction Counseling. *Rehabilitation Counseling Bulletin 43*, 209 – 215. (Download from Norwich University Expanded Academic ASAP.)

Shulman, L. (1992). *The Skills of Helping: Individuals, Families, and Groups* (3rd Ed.), Itasca, IL: F.E. Peacock Publishers, Inc.

Stewart, J. (Ed.). (1999). *Bridges Not Walls: A Book About Interpersonal Communication* (7th Ed.). Boston: McGraw-Hill College.

Substance Abuse and Mental Health Services Administration. (1999) *Brief Interventions and Brief Therapies for Substance Abuse.* Rockville, MD: Author

Thombs, D. (1994). *Introduction to Addictive Behaviors.* New York: The Guilford Press

Trimpey, J. (1989). *The Small Book.* New York: Delacorte Press

Trimpey, J. (1996). *Rational Recovery: The New Cure for Substance Addiction.* New York: Pocket Books

Walant, K. (1995). *Creating the Capacity for Attachment: Treating Addictions and the Alienanted Self.* Northvale, N.J.: Jason Aronson Inc.

White, W (2001, April). A Disease Concept for the 21ˢᵗ Century. *Counselor: The Magazine for Addiction Professionals, 2,* pp.48-52.

White, W & Miller W (2007, August) The Use of Confrontation in Addiction Treatment. *Counselor: The Magazine for Addiction Professionals, 4,* pp.12-30.

Winger, G., Hofmann, F., & Woods, J. (1992). *A Handbook on Drug and Alcohol Abuse: The Biomedical Aspects.* New York, NY: Oxford University Press.

Yalom, I. (1995). *The Theory and Practice of Group Psychotherapy.* (Fourth Edition). New York: Basic Books

Other Resources

Websites:

www.naadac.org – NAADAC, the Association for Addiction Professionals, represents the professional interests of more than 75,000 addiction counselors, educators and other addiction-focused health care professionals in the United States, Canada and abroad. NAADAC's members are addiction counselors, educators and other addiction-focused health care professionals, who specialize in addiction prevention, treatment, recovery support and education. An important part of the healthcare continuum, NAADAC members and its 44 state affiliates work to create healthier individuals, families and communities through prevention, intervention, quality treatment and recovery support.

www.samhsa.gov - The Substance Abuse and Mental Health Services Administration (SAMHSA) is the agency within the U.S. Department of Health and Human Services that leads public health efforts to advance the behavioral health of the nation. SAMHSA's mission is to reduce the impact of substance abuse and mental illness on America's communities. The site has a lot of good information, including an on-line treatment locator and a lot of free books and other information. They have an excellent Anger Management program with books for the group leader as well as for participants that is designed for addicted clients.

www.aatod.org - The American Association for the Treatment of Opioid Dependence (AATOD) was founded in 1984 to enhance the quality of patient care in treatment programs by promoting the growth and development of comprehensive opioid treatment services throughout the United States. This site offers many useful resources for counselors.

www.suboxone.com - This site offers information for patients, prescribers, and therapists. It includes a search program that allows patients to find prescribers in their area; this is helpful for counselors who want to connect with their local doctors.

www.vivitrol.com – On this site you can find information about the use of Vivitrol for alcohol dependence and opiate dependence. There is a section for health professionals that offers a lot of useful information.

www.motivationalinterview.org - This site is the best resource for information on MI. The materials included here are designed to facilitate the dissemination, adoption and implementation of MI among clinicians, supervisors, program managers and trainers, and improve treatment outcomes for clients with substance use disorders.

www.positivepathcounseling.org – This is the webpage for my counseling practice, but there is also information about Positive Path Recovery there. There is also contact information; I am always willing to offer information and answer questions.

About the Author

Gary Blanchard began his career in the addiction treatment field after graduation from College of Notre Dame of Maryland's Weekend College in 1998. In 2000, Gary enrolled in Vermont College of Norwich University; he received a Masters in Addictions Counseling from Vermont College in 2002.

Since moving to West Brookfield, Massachusetts, in 2006, Gary worked in programs for people with co-occurring disorders. He started the Positive Path Counseling Center in 2007; he retired from his private practice in June 2018. Gary teaches at Holyoke Community College in Holyoke, Massachusetts and at Anna Maria College in Paxton, Massachusetts. He is a licensed alcohol and drug counselor; in 2014 he was named Counselor of the Year by the Massachusetts Association of Alcohol and Drug Abuse Counselors (MAADAC). Gary currently offers counseling through 413 Therapy Group in Western Massachusetts.

Gary is the author of *Positive Path Recovery: A Clinician's Guide, Counseling for Medication Assisted Recovery, Keeping Your Cool: An Anger Management Guide,* and *Building and Maintaining Recovery.* He has presented at many local and national conferences. He is Past President of MAADAC.

Made in the USA
Middletown, DE
30 July 2021